The Big Machine

G. T. EMERY

1970

Translated by
Grace Marmor Spruch and Traude Wess
Illustrated with photographs

ROBERT JUNGK

The
Big
Machine

CHARLES SCRIBNER'S SONS · NEW YORK

For my son

Contents

v

Illustrations

following page 88

ONE

The Research Factory

I

Not long ago, when I read in my morning paper that the proton synchroton at CERN, in Meyrin, near Geneva, one of the two largest accelerators in the world, had broken down the night before and would presumably be out of action for some months, the news, probably not of any interest or even comprehensible to most readers, hit me as personally as would the report that a close friend had been in an accident.

A few years ago the news would not have meant much to me either. It is true that I had dealt with atomic questions before, but as to the actual purpose of a synchrotron, or the difference between atomic and nuclear research, I was as unclear as anyone. I certainly was not aware that among scientists and engineers the "Big Machine" at Meyrin is considered one of the great cultural achievements of our time, the contemporary counterpart of the temples of antiquity, the cathedrals of the Middle Ages, and the monumental palaces of later centuries.

The strange word CERN, however, was not unknown to me. The first time I heard it—it must have been in 1955—was when the German physicist Wolfgang Gentner agreed to grant me an interview.

"I will be in Geneva by that time, at CERN," he informed me. "That is where you can most likely find me."

As things turned out, though, Professor Gentner had caught a bad cold—presumably on the construction site of this CERN— and so, instead of getting together at Meyrin or Geneva's Cointrin airport, we met in a comfortable tavern in town. The subject of our discussion was the difficult matter of conscience confronting atomic scientists through the military use of their earth-shaking discoveries. Gentner, who ordinarily inclines toward jokes full of self-irony, was plainly depressed by these developments. From the dismal background of depression the word CERN emerged all the brighter each time it was mentioned. Whenever the scientist uttered it, there was a note of enthusiasm and hope in his voice, which I noticed but could not fully appreciate then.

I was to hear this note more and more often in the years to come. My book* on the tragic situation in which atomic scientists found themselves—to which Professor Gentner had contributed his impressions—had been published in the meantime, and was being discussed vehemently even among the protagonists. I often found myself involved in debate with physicists, therefore, on the course of development of these newly released forces so overshadowed by guilt and doubt. In the midst of these discussions, as soon as doubts were expressed about the future of scientific progress, an impressive argument was put forth:

* *Brighter than a Thousand Suns* (Harcourt, Brace and World, Inc., 1958).

2

"Yes, but CERN. . . ."

CERN, as I learned, is an acronym for Conseil Européen pour la Recherche Nucléaire (European Council for Nuclear Research), an organization established after World War II by a dozen European nations for the purpose of sponsoring "research of a pure scientific and fundamental character."

"Atom and hydrogen bombs have absolutely no place in the work done at CERN," an official of the International Atomic Energy Agency in Vienna explained. "Although, technologically, these are highly complex war toys, from a scientific standpoint the problems that arise nowadays in their production and 'improvement' are of less than secondary importance. The frontiers of physics are no longer to be found in the weapons laboratories but in the high-energy physics laboratories: in the American research centers of Berkeley, Argonne, and Brookhaven; in the Soviet 'atomic city,' Dubna; and in Europe at CERN in Meyrin. There, some of the old carefree spirit of research lives again. There, the family of nuclear physicists, scattered by politics and war, is again united."

"Can you get me an introduction to the director of one of these institutions?"

"Oh, but you don't need an introduction! Anyone who is really interested can get a permit to visit CERN or the other research centers I mentioned."

So one day I headed for those new territories. What started out as a quick reconnaissance trip turned into a long journey, for one cannot get to know a high-energy physics laboratory in a single brief visit. As my colleague Paul O'Neil of *Life* once remarked, one must experience and explore it as one would a distant exotic land, whose inhabitants speak a language not recorded in any dictionary and live an extremely unusual mode of existence. In retrospect it seems to me that modern research centers are territories less separated from us in space than in time: harbingers of the future penetrating into the present.

3

II

From Geneva's main station to Meyrin—a village that has recently become the first "satellite city in Switzerland," and whose western part CERN borders—is just about fifteen or twenty minutes by car, traffic permitting, on a smooth, hilly road to Lyon.

The bus took at least twice that long, since it serves the residential areas fanning out from the road. But this detour was a better preparation for CERN than the direct route by taxi.

The once idyllic gardens and farmland between Geneva and the Jura chain, which inspired Rousseau to sing the praises of nature, are being transformed inexorably into a residential area for thousands, and are now the chaotic scene of hasty, reckless urbanization. True, there are building regulations here, just as in the outskirts of almost all large cities, to maintain a "green belt." But the remaining encircled *jardiniers, vignerons,* and *patrons* of rustic *auberges* with quaint names have long since given up their hopeless struggle against the invasion of the big housing developments, the spread-legged supports for high-tension wires, and the incessant shrieking of the jets taking off from Cointrin airport. These people probably look forward to the day when the laws that now protect their land will be repealed, so that they can leave their remaining barren meadows to the bulldozers and steamrollers—for an exorbitant price.

I was able to imagine, after the bus ride, what it would look like later: holes in the ground, in which yesterday's rain and the day before yesterday's generate filthy puddles. Black roads still smelling of tar. Along their muddy yellow edges the multi-storied glass egg boxes housing the new tenants. Somewhere up on the eighth floor a lone tricycle, or on the eleventh a folded parasol or a coat hanging out for brushing. In the midst of all these rust-colored piles of clutter, neon signs of a supermarket, scrawny lampposts, temporary-looking cables set off against a light blue sky filled with the white spume of exhaust pipes.

4

This unfinished, temporary state of the new Geneva suburbs continues into the adjacent site of CERN. When I first looked at it from the traffic-filled road, I saw construction rather than buildings: open ditches, mounds of loose earth with pieces of concrete pipe piled beside them, along with the roar of hydraulic drills, milling machines, welding equipment, and starting motors—all this did not conform to my notion of the isolated ivory towers of science.

Such commotion is not unusual. As I discovered later, it is standard operation for CERN. Mallet, the French construction engineer in charge of *Sites et Bâtiments* at the time, remarked: "I believe that in each and every working day in the history of this laboratory somewhere on the premises something was either built or rebuilt. Here we are never finished." And a fellow countryman of his, the geologist Jean Gervaise, added, with a glance at the construction machinery churning away outside his window: *"Si le CERN ne bouge plus, le CERN sera mort."* (If CERN no longer moves, CERN will die.)

III

I stood at the open gate of the main entrance to the premises and waited for the uniformed guard to ask what I wanted and demand my credentials. But he had no time for me, for he was busy talking to the driver of a car. Impatient, I took a few steps toward the nearby administration building. Then I stopped and turned to see whether the roadside conference had been concluded. But the two men were still chatting unperturbed. So I went a little farther. The official would call me back anyway.

No such thing! When next I turned, he was walking slowly toward the gatehouse. Had he not seen me pass by? I tried to attract his attention by calling; I did not want to encounter any difficulties. Finally he turned toward me. But even then he did not call me back; he simply waved me on.

Nowadays we expect guards at national or international institutions to be suspicious and strict, to ask questions, demand papers, to telephone some higher official, and only after all kinds of formalities to let the visitor pass, as though he had just been granted a pardon. Man is as accustomed to these pressures as he is to gravity. If they are unexpectedly not exercised, the person who never questions authority finds himself completely confused. He begins to quaver inside, then to quake, to lose ground under his feet. In this strange state I drifted toward the entrance to the administration building, white in the midst of green meadows, its windows glittering in the sun.

My faint euphoria was to become even more pronounced when, after climbing a few steps, I reached a high portal and entered a spacious hall. For what met my ears were the notes of a piano concerto. Mozart? Rather unusual at eleven in the morning, in the middle of a workday.

The people I saw moving about in no particular hurry seemed to find it perfectly normal. Some stood in front of a counter, others went to see what the bulletin boards had to offer. Outside a cafeteria, near a newspaper stand, a small group of men sipped their espressos as casually as if they were in the center of an Italian piazza.

I had actually wanted to ask for the information desk, but the music, which seemed to come from upstairs, drew me on. I followed the sound by climbing a section of the double staircase opposite the entrance and arrived in a sunlit gallery.

My first glance fell on a pair of glasses lying in the middle of the tile floor as if they had been lost. My second went to a young man with a crew-cut playing an old-fashioned instrument with his eyes closed. He was, I learned later, a visiting theoretical physicist from the United States, who had just made a controversial name for himself through a new interpretation of subnuclear phenomena considered rather mad. "This is how he gets his inspiration," I was told later.

From up there I could see into a bright corridor connecting the administration building with the others. A knot of people moved slowly toward me through this glass-enclosed passage. Next to a tall, pale Scandinavian were two younger men in white open-necked sport shirts and a somewhat older, more mature-looking man who appeared to be a Pole or a Czech. A small Japanese fellow was drawn along in their wake. He listened attentively, while the others, paying not the slightest heed to the music, argued vigorously and stopped every now and then to watch the main speaker draw a curve in the air with his index finger, as if he were standing before a blackboard.

Since I could not make out the words, which were drowned by the strains of the sonata, I turned and looked down on a beautiful courtyard. There, surrounded by green plants, a tree in blossom, and the remains of ancient pillars, was a white-tiled octagonal pool with black and white geometric patterns on its flat bottom: counterpoint of silence in the commotion of the corridors.

Looking from above across the pool, I discovered my group of disputants on the other side of the reflecting octagon; they had reached the ground floor in the meantime. They had settled themselves near a window in the cafeteria, at a table not yet cleared. Others had joined them. All were talking at once with excited gestures and expressions. Then one laughed. The others joined in, and all relaxed in one concerted outburst of contagious mirth.

IV

To the uninitiated a first visit to CERN is, more than anything else, highly confusing. He knows he is going to see a laboratory, and he therefore has certain preconceptions. But what he actually sees exceeds by far what he had anticipated, in terms of buildings and machinery. It is virtually an entire city. There, one finds not only a post office, bank, travel bureau, and nursery school but a power plant, sewage disposal system, cooling towers, and garages as well. There is also a widespread network of

7

asphalt streets, along which are workshops, laboratories, office buildings, and computing centers.

What is the purpose of all these tank trucks, vehicles, and cranes? What do the more than two thousand people working with hundreds of pieces of apparatus in day and night shifts produce, at a yearly cost of nearly $35 million? The end product weighs very little: it is "only" letters and numbers. Through them theoretical physicists attempt to formulate concepts—which are becoming increasingly intricate, but to their minds, increasingly precise—of a material world no longer directly perceptible through human senses.

These mathematical symbols are the final distillation of millions of pieces of information, recorded photographically or magnetically, on processes occurring in the interior of nuclear particles, processes with inconceivably short durations, occurring in a region where a hundredth of an inch is as large as a continent and a second lasts a century. These recordings of the comings and goings in the subnuclear sphere constitute the statistical raw material which leads to new curves, new formulae, and new theories on the structure of matter. The enormous number of nuclear events produced in the accelerators and detected by special instruments is compressed and abstracted by computers and other devices to such an extent that CERN's annual intellectual output can be contained in a few hundred pages, and the most sought after, truly significant results in a few thin but weighty papers.

People taking the Saturday guided tour through the research factory at Meyrin find it extremely hard to comprehend that such a huge plant—it covers more than two hundred acres on both sides of the French-Swiss border—cannot produce anything more "usable," more "tangible." The guides whose task it is to shepherd the visitors through Geneva's new tourist attraction attempt, with infinite patience, to explain this extraordinary phenomenon of a large-scale industrial enterprise that manufactures neither a finished nor even a half-finished product.

I never tired of listening to these young teachers and students as they talked to the people they showed around.

"But do you generate atomic power at least?" someone asked insistently.

"No, reactors do that. Here, there are accelerators. They use power. A great deal, as a matter of fact: about twelve percent of Geneva's total consumption."

"What happens in these acc—"

"Accelerators. They accelerate tiny bunches of the elementary particles which form the nucleus of the hydrogen atom, the so-called protons, by causing them to revolve within the machine until they travel at almost the velocity of light. Then, at this high energy, the protons are made to hit a metal target. The target particles break up under the heavy bombardment and give rise to new, different particles, which can be observed with the aid of special detectors."

"What do these—these protons look like? Like specks of dust? Drops of water? Dots? Triangles?"

"We have never seen them ourselves. Nobody has ever seen them. Only the tracks they leave behind and the effects they cause can be recorded."

"But you just spoke about 'bunches.' What do you mean by that?"

No, CERN's guides really don't have it easy. They must attempt to bring to the visitors the concepts of modern physics, which are not accessible to ordinary imagination. When they say that nuclear research must make use of symbols and models which cannot be represented pictorially and can only be expressed with any degree of precision in mathematical terms, heads nod, mouths murmur: *"Extraordinaire!"*—*"Das ist ja phantastisch!"*—or "I begin to grasp it," but expressions of bewilderment and perplexity belie these assurances. Visitors somehow stand lost in this manner, between thick black cables, surrounded by colorful wires spreading like creeping vines, staring at green curves of light behind glass oscilloscope screens, that

9

flash yellow, orange, and red lights on control panels, experiencing the miracle of science as naïvely as they experience the beauty of nature—but perhaps not less deeply.

This uncritical awe has been unfairly ridiculed by some scientists. They have forgotten, unfortunately, that there was a time when they too could not understand all that; and perhaps it was the very mystery of that other world that stimulated their choice of profession.

I also underwent the same experiences as the CERN tourists during my first visits to Meyrin: I was impressed, but more than that, confused, and I could not admit it at the time, either to my hosts or to myself. I ended by trying to tell myself, as consolation, that I was interested mainly in the people who work there, in the way they live together and handle their problems, as well as in the history and the future of this international community. That was what I wanted to learn about, not this difficult subject, physics, with which all these people struggle. But I soon came to realize that I could not get an understanding of the scientists until I had a clearer understanding of their work. It was then that I discovered that at CERN I had encountered an obstacle harder to get around than ordinary bureaucractic red tape: my own ignorance. That is a wall that one can bang one's head against in vain, a wall built from an accumulation of omissions and pretenses and reinforced by false pride.

And all kinds of well-meaning consolers wanted to see to it that things remained that way. It was that way not only with me, they would tell me. Progress in all the natural sciences long ago made ignoramuses out of "educated" people. We have to content ourselves with simply accepting the effects on our lives initiated by the work done in the laboratories, experiencing them, and suffering them. In order to understand them more fully, one needs the leisure and, moreover, the ability to absorb, which very few have these days. Who has the time and the energy, as an adult, to sit on a school bench again?

The first narrow breach in these defenses was made by a

friendly Dutch girl, a teacher in the nursery school at the edge of CERN's territory.

When, on one of my tours, I saw some paintings and collages exhibited on the schoolroom walls, it suddenly became clear to me: here at CERN I have actually become a child again. I understand as much of the world disclosed by physicists as does a three- or four-year-old of his surroundings.

The teacher must have noticed my startled expression when I looked at a round scrap of paper pasted on a colorful cardboard background, from which hung two long strips of brown glazed paper. She tried to explain her pupil's work of art:

"That is how little Charlie sees a man. But you know children learn exceedingly fast."

V

One of my best teachers at CERN was a round-faced, stocky Sicilian brimming over with vitality and words, Antonio Zichichi. He is a very successful and well-known experimentalist, but he hardly shows it, and talks to the layman as if he were someone to be taken seriously and not as most physicists assume, a hopeless case.

Actually I got together with Zichichi only three or four times. But it was always he who turned the key and opened a door closed to me up to then.

"Simple, isn't it?" he would finish by saying, right after having compared subnuclear processes and events to things edible. These "bunches of grapes," "raisin cakes," and "Swiss cheeses" were certainly nutritious images. The mind not familiar with quantum mechanics and matrix calculations was supposed to swallow and metabolize them—and then immediately to forget about them.

In this way my tutor from Trapani helped me overcome my initial confusion concerning the size, variety, and complexity of CERN.

At lunch one day, we sat at one of the long tables in the cafeteria, among engineers, physicists, administrators, and foreign visitors, this time eating real food, when Zichichi began: "What exactly is an experiment? First, someone has an idea. He examines—or has others examine—whether or not his assumptions are in accordance with nature. This is the way physics has been done since the days of Galileo. Step two: the experimenter sets up a series of tests. Step three: with their help he tries to generate certain processes which can be recorded and controlled. Step four: he observes, measures, and compares. Step five: he analyzes and publishes. Do you by any chance know the apparatus with which Rutherford carried out the experiments leading to the discovery of the atomic nucleus?"

"Yes," I said, "it is in the Cavendish Laboratory. I even saw it with my own eyes. It is on exhibit there in a small glass case."

"Yes, Rutherford was once photographed with it. But if one of us here wanted to be photographed with his equipment, for everything used today in a single test a composite photograph made up of a dozen exposures would not suffice. There lies—at least superficially—the main difference between then and now: in the changed dimensions! Where once a study or an office was large enough, now not even a building is adequate, hardly even an establishment like this one. For we need a hundred times more and a hundred times larger instruments, in order to get to the point where we can discover something really new. Basically we still do the same things we did before. We have only"—and he spread both his arms wide as if to embrace not only all of CERN but an area reaching at least as far as Sicily—"expanded slightly."

VI

The enormously increased outlay of machines and finances in order to penetrate the unplumbed depths of matter can be compared, in many respects, to the growing cost of grasping for the far reaches of the cosmos. Astronomy and space research have, since 1945, expanded outward the sphere reached by man with the aid of his instruments—to a degree hardly realized by the man in the street—while, during the same period, high-energy physics has penetrated deeper than ever inward. That rockets and telescopes should become larger and costlier is obvious. In a comparable manner the power and dimensions of accelerators and detectors must also continually increase, for it is with these that the nuclear physicists penetrate to the world of inconceivably small dimensions and incomprehensibly short times.

As early as 1927, Ernest Rutherford realized that beams of high-energy particles could be used as probes for a more precise investigation of the atomic nucleus, which is protected by powerful electrical barriers. In the course of three decades physicists succeeded in increasing, in several steps, the energy of their accelerators more than 50,000 times: from 600,000 electron volts first to several million and finally to 33 billion electron volts.

It all happened at so great a rate that some of the physicists who, as young men, had worked with the modest, easily handled instruments of atomic and beginning nuclear physics, in their primes became the directors of entire industrial laboratory complexes.

One of these men is Victor F. Weisskopf. Born in Vienna in 1908, he began his career in Göttingen toward the end of the twenties, and, after thirty years in the laboratories and lecture halls of Zurich, Copenhagen, Kharkov, Rochester, Los Alamos, and Cambridge (Massachusetts), in 1961 was appointed Director-General of CERN. As he had seen in his own lifetime the evolution from the idyllic university laboratory of the old days to the large-scale nuclear research plant of today, I wanted to ask him whether the immense buildup of research apparatus could not have been avoided.

"Viki" (as he is called in the overgrown family of physicists) is one of the very few scientists who can see beyond the limits of their individual specialties. This gives him a breadth, which, although it has become increasingly hard to find in this profession, became an essential ingredient of the "spirit of CERN" during the years he headed the nuclear research center. Weisskopf's appreciation of the miracle of science, his tolerance, and his sense of humor were already manifest in his outer office. Its walls were covered with the fantastic crayon drawings of a "crazy inventor" who, for years, unselfishly sent CERN his multicolored drafts of machines propelled by the light of distant stars or the "music of the spheres."

"Isn't it possible that the gigantic machines that the physicists have built and are planning to build are similar products of fantastic notions?" I asked Weisskopf.

He overlooked the provocation, thought a while, and asked in return: "Were there any other choices for nuclear physics?" He uttered this, it seemed to me, in a manner more regretful than triumphant, and rose slowly to pace to and fro in his office. "In only forty years we have lived through three periods of nuclear physics. In the first we dealt primarily with the shell of the atom. At that time, a few volts were enough to kick several electrons out of an atom. Then came the second stage: the study of the atomic nucleus, held together by tremendous forces. In order to overcome them, energies of several hundred thousand to a million electron volts were required. That happened in the thirties. In the period after World War II the third stage followed naturally: the investigation of the particles found in the atomic nucleus, the so-called nucleons. That is possible only if we mobilize billions of volts to make beams of high-energy particles hit other particles. It is for that that we need these enormous machines."

"Strange! The instruments become more and more huge, while the subject of the investigation becomes tinier and tinier?"

"Yes, that seems paradoxical. But according to a fundamental and profound precept of quantum physics, the smaller the subject, the higher the energy necessary to investigate it. An increasingly precise knowledge of matter depends, therefore, on building increasingly powerful instruments. No physicist likes largeness for largeness' sake. But up to now we have found no other way."

The director's office, where this conversation took place, can no longer be the scholar's study of the time of Rutherford and Arnold Sommerfeld in this age of "Big Science"—an expression analogous to "big business," coined by the American physicist Alvin Weinberg in a deliberate attempt at polemic—but has become instead a decision-making order-giving center in constant contact with the entire world. With all that, the director of such a center must try to avoid acting like a manager and, as the head of a community of scientists, must run his institute in academic fashion. Weisskopf, for example, made an effort to remain active in research during his time in office, in spite of the many administrative and official duties he had to perform, and, whenever possible, held a weekly seminar on the latest developments in theoretical physics.

It is true, though, that a scientific enterprise does not have as well-defined goals and as traditional an administrative structure as an economic or a national organization. It is in many respects similar to a big expedition exploring unknown territories.

I had first heard this comparison during my conversation with Professor Gentner. Later I read a more precise formulation of the idea in a paper Gentner sent me with a remark, characteristic of him: "Please criticize!" The text read: "The difference between an expedition to a dot on the map and an expedition to the interior of the atom is that the map of the atoms is not yet even finished, and therefore one does not know for certain where the dots—in particular, the interesting ones —are to be found. For this reason, in the scholarly republic at large research centers, before anything else there is always endless discussion of the aims of the next large project. For the aims are foggy, and only from vague outlines can those with the sharpest eyes suggest a possible new path."

But where and when do these disputes on future experiments take place? When I wanted to find that out during the first days of my visit to CERN, I asked Roger Anthoine, head of the information service, and accustomed to "stupid" questions. He replied drily: "All the time. Everywhere." Indeed, I learned that the meetings of the various scientific committees, where the next experiments and the next after them are debated and scheduled, are actually no more than the very last stage of a large never-ending conversation buzzing through all the nuclear physics laboratories of the world and all the rooms of the Geneva institute.

Sometimes it starts where it really should start, namely, in the theoreticians' offices, where the doors are usually wide open, so that anyone passing by who is interested in the discussion going on in front of the blackboard can join in easily. But more often I heard these passionate debates in physicists' jargon, hardly a word of which the layman understands, in the corridors after a lecture by a prominent visitor, in the meeting rooms before or after a seminar, in the South Hall's small tea room during a night shift—above all, during meals or over coffee. The paper tablecloths, scribbled full of numbers, formulae, and curves on these occasions are often taken back to offices. Many a venture into the unknown began in this informal way.

VII

"PS"—the abbreviation for proton synchrotron—is the prosaic name of the Big Machine at Meyrin. It was given to it by its designers only provisionally at first, but it came into established use after such high-flown terms as "eurotron" and "billiotron" proved unacceptable.

Construction of the PS was the actual motive for establishing CERN. The realization that so large, complicated, and costly an instrument as the PS could not be supported by a single nation led to the joint establishment by a dozen nations of an international laboratory. Today thirteen nations belong to this Conseil Européen pour la Recherche Nucléaire, sharing the costs according to their national incomes.* The largest contribution comes from the Federal Republic of Germany, the lowest from Greece. Almost two thirds of the entire burden is carried by the "big four" (Germany, Britain, France, Italy). The number of countries whose citizens are to be found at CERN is much larger, however. For, in addition to people from the member states and the three nations officially belonging to the Council as "observers" (Poland, Turkey, and Yugoslavia), visitors from the Soviet Union, Japan, India, the United States, and many other nations are always to be found at CERN.† Sometimes they stay for several days, sometimes for weeks or even years.

In addition to the 28 BeV (billion electron volt) PS, there is at CERN another, smaller machine, the 600 million electron volt SC (short for synchro-cyclotron); although this atom smasher is one of the most powerful machines in its class, the PS is the actual core of CERN, the central, decisive stimulus for all the nuclear physics laboratories of the world.

I was astonished, therefore, when one of the experimenters I questioned about the Big Machine remarked: "I have worked with it for quite a while. But I have never seen it close up, and I have never seen it in its entirety." That was the case because the place where he worked was very far from the PS, for he was in one of the laboratories using a "secondary beam," originally generated in the machine, then transformed and directed through hundreds of yards of pipes.

It is not very easy to get close to the machine, as the most important parts of this ten-thousand-ton instrument are buried in a

---

* Austria (1.90%), Belgium (3.56%), Denmark (2.05%), Federal Republic of Germany (23.30%), France (19.34%), Great Britain (22.16%), Greece (0.60%), Italy (11.24%), Netherlands (3.88%), Norway (1.41%), Spain (3.43%), Sweden (4.02%), Switzerland (3.11%).
† Scientists from the People's Republic of China have also been invited, but thus far none have accepted.

highly shielded subterranean tunnel for protection against harmful radiation. Only a limited number of persons have access to the tunnel, during periods when the machine is not in operation. The magnets, high-frequency apparatus, vacuum pumps, and the almost evacuated circular chamber in which the accelerated particles travel at high speed are all familiar to the laboratory members from diagrams, seldom from direct experience.

During one of the week-long inspections the accelerator undergoes at regular intervals, I was allowed to climb down into the artificially lit concrete ring, which has television cameras trained on all its entrances, and could walk along the entire 2,040-foot underground circle that the hydrogen particles travel millions of times in seconds. But I did not have a true picture of the outer dimensions of the PS until I flew from the Geneva airport to Zurich one day and looked down from the plane, which passes almost directly over CERN.

There it was below me: this horizontal Ferris wheel almost one third mile around, its spokes—the control passages converging in the center—each more than one hundred yards long. The outlines could be made out clearly, as the hills piled up for protection against radiation and now covered with grass follow the ground plan exactly. Seen from the air the structure reminds one of an excavation site of ancient ruins, a gigantic burial mound or some other pagan shrine. It was only then that I could appreciate what Professor Faissner, a CERN researcher, meant when he said to me one night during a walk:

"Suppose our civilization were to be destroyed in an atomic war, and rediscovered centuries later by the descendants of the few survivors. What would they think this was, this gigantic circular structure, precise to thousandths of an inch? Most probably it would be taken for a place of worship. Please don't laugh at this idea. For I ask myself sometimes in all seriousness whether all that goes on at CERN cannot be considered a kind of worship, a worship in the language of our so-called scientific age, of course—a seeking, a striving for something greater, for truth, if that is what you want to call it. Probably this striving will never end. People before us discovered particles in the nuclei of atoms, and in those particles we find even smaller constituents. With larger and more powerful instruments scientists might make out even finer structure, even tinier building stones. In this way, mankind will gain greater insight into a variety of regions still unknown, and will presumably never come to the end. But are we not doing the same thing that people tried to do before in a different way: they erected temples for their worship."

We went on a few steps, in silence. I asked: "Then, would research be today's newest form of praying, perhaps?"

VIII

The inside of one of CERN's large experimental halls, as seen from a high passageway along the wall, reminds one of a wild romantic mountain landscape. Gray boulders rise up to form steep walls. Bridges and footpaths, with flashing red lights and purple triangles warning of radioactivity beside them, lead over ridges and gorges at the bottom of which run ducts made of long sections of pipe. Through these ducts at least six or seven, sometimes up to nine, different research teams are connected to the central apparatus, for it is never the case that only a single experiment is carried out on the proton synchrotron. In addition to the teams that have priority on the beam coming from the Big Machine, there are also the so-called "parasites," who can direct into their measuring instruments only the remainder of the precious particles. The scientists' lairs, packed with all kinds of apparatus and, in most cases, covered only with corrugated paper or enormous black cloths, look like provisional campsites put up for a few nights. The Promethean landscape under the floodlights also has no permanence. Enormous cranes attached to the ceiling approach like rolling thunder, and the bare rocks, the dangerous cliffs, turn out to be concrete shielding blocks, easily dismantled and quickly removed by powerful instruments.

The scene is especially impressive at night. In the administration building the lights are out, but in the library, which never closes its doors, in the computing center, in the control rooms of the two accelerators, and in the experimental halls, there is always commotion. Except for repair periods, the Big Machine and its little "sister" are always in operation, to enable the research teams to get as many shifts as possible for their measurements. The scientists want to make full use of the precious, all-too-short machine time, even if it means days and nights of hectic activity and no sleep.

There is continuous contact by intercom between the men in green overalls or white coats camped in the experimental halls in front of their hundred-eyed switchboards, and the central control room of the PS, so that the intensity and tempo of the machine can be adjusted to the needs of the clientele, the researchers. From the standpoint of the user, the technical miracle —the proton synchrotron—despite its size and complexity, is looked upon essentially as some kind of water pipe, out of which he expects billions of the proper particles to flow at regular intervals.

The generation of a beam of high energy and intensity (that is, containing as many particles as possible) is actually only the first phase of the experiment. The protons accelerated by successive electrical impulses to a velocity of almost 186,000 miles per second are transformed into dense bursts of new particles of an amazing variety, after colliding with a thin wire of aluminum, beryllium, copper, or gold. The three "fundamental building blocks" of the atom spoken of even as late as the end of the twenties—proton, neutron, and electron—have since increased, through constant new discoveries, to more than one hundred different particles, each with its own unique qualities, and this subnuclear "population explosion" has not yet come to an end.

Out of this abundance of k-ons, pions, antiprotons, neutrons, hyperons, rho-mesons, and whatever else they are called, produced by each proton impact on the metal "target," out of this well-stocked "zoo of strange beasts," as Robert Oppenheimer once put it, the experimenter would like possibly only one kind of particle for his current experiment. Thus, an unbelievably fast and complicated process of separating, sorting, and directing must occur, in view of the infinitesimally short lifetimes of the particles, varying between a millionth of a second and a millionth of a millionth of a millionth of a second.

The art of "beam handling" and "beam separation," developed within the last few years, arose through the discovery, refinement, and increasingly skillful use of a number of special precision instruments. With their aid the bunches of protons are directed onto a target; then the secondary particles are sent through a filter system of magnets, electrostatic fields—"lenses" of field lines of various kinds and strengths—and electronic counters, until they are isolated and separated according to mass, velocity, and charge. The infinitely small and short-lived are handled as securely and naturally as if creatures of the macrocosmos were being produced, separated, and distributed.

Special teams of mathematicians, machine physicists, magnet specialists, electrical engineers, and skilled mechanics often work for months on the up to two-hundred-meter-long "paths" for a filtered beam, paths composed of pipes, switches, power supplies, and magnets. Then they write a report such as the following: "Measurements with the Čerenkov counter showed 12 negative k-ons accompanied by about 6 muons. The intensity was intentionally reduced, and the photographs show an average of 7 k-ons per burst with only five to at most ten percent contamination by other particles. We obtained this beam by previously eliminating undesirable particles one hundred times more numerous."

IX

Only after this difficult sorting process can the actual observation of the particles' subsequent behavior begin. In the early fifties, when the decision to establish CERN was made, the methods for sorting were few, and the detectors were primitive and inaccurate. With the new generation of Big Machines came the development of a host of detecting devices, which, just as was the case with accelerators, became not only more complicated and faster but also, unfortunately, larger and costlier. The "bubble chamber" which, together with the "spark chamber," is the most commonly used instrument today for the detection and observation of subnuclear processes, was only about an inch long and half an inch wide at the time of its invention by the twenty-six-year-old American physicist Donald Glaser of the University of Michigan (Ann Arbor). Supposedly, the foam adhering to a beer glass gave the inventor the idea of sending gamma-rays through hop liquid, in the hope that their tracks would become visible. The experiment was unsuccessful, but experiments using superheated ether and, later, propane did prove successful. Electrically charged particles, in passing through these liquids heated to just above their boiling points, left behind microscopically small bubbles of vapor that remained visible as lines for several microseconds and thus clearly marked the paths of the nuclear particles.

When, in 1952, Glaser sent to the *Physical Review* the first photograph of his "chamber" (which from the outside looked like an electric light bulb) together with a description, the editor knew so little about the new invention that he had the picture printed upside down.

In only fifteen years this small instrument grew into the present mammoth bubble chambers. They weigh hundreds of tons, fill entire laboratories, and their construction requires years of work of hundreds of specialists. While Glaser could finance the prototype of the bubble chamber out of a grant of less than $1,000, the construction costs of the largest chambers planned today are estimated at $10 million to $20 million for each. The decided advantage of the bubble chamber over the detecting devices used earlier (the cloud chamber, for example) is that it shows greater detail and more events, and operates incomparably faster. Thousands of photographs of nuclear processes can be taken within a few hours; and today, at CERN, where two or three bubble chambers of different sizes are continously in operation, many more than two million bubble chamber pictures can be produced annually. The world production in 1965 amounted to about ten million pictures, and, according to estimates of Dr. William Fowler (Brookhaven), by 1975 it will have increased to forty million exposures per annum.

Among my most impressive experiences at CERN are the minutes during which I could witness, through a thick glass wall, the birth-and-death drama of nuclear particles. In the abrupt, swift illuminations of the flash lamps the observer sees constantly changing but always magically beautiful images. On a gleaming purple background there appears a delicate structure of faint white circles, lines, angles, stars. Just as he wants to examine it in all its rhythmic variety, behind the oval glass window it is black again. But now another, an even more exciting picture flares up: on seven or eight staff lines there is a small explosion; a tiny satellite is cast off and falls, falls, until it vanishes in tall grass that splits and disseminates tiny spores, from which a screen of thin silver wires grows up to the sky. Then—again darkness. The ear distinguishes a loud rhythmic beating and pounding: it comes from the pistons with which the chamber pressure is suddenly decreased, causing the rapidly cooled liquid to boil. Fractions of seconds later another salvo of particles is fired: the light flash reveals a landscape of frosted needles forming vines, thistles, a tall sunflower on a tapered, symmetrically branching stem. One of the open triangles ejects a whirling spiral into the sinking landscape.

This exciting ballet of the birth, death, and transfiguration of the elementary particles is hardly ever witnessed by the members of a bubble chamber team, and when it is, then only to make sure that everything is under control. Even the physicists who later look through the photographic records of the subnuclear events exhibit as little interest in the highly esthetic pictures, which remind one of abstract art, as would a map maker or a field marshal in the beauties of a landscape.

In the physicists' language microcosmic processes are described in a completely different (and, of course, more "correct") way: "That is a k-minus with an energy of 5 BeV. At this point a xi-minus is produced. The k-minus collided with a proton. In the process a pi-meson is created, and a k-zero as well. At this point it decays into a pi-minus and a pi-plus. The xi-minus, a cascade particle, reaches that point over there. It is heavy and, therefore, rather slow. Here, it decays into a pi-minus and a lambda-zero. The lambda goes on to that point over there, and also decays, into a proton and a pi-minus."

Should the hairline tracks on the photograph indicate to the expert events* from which he can draw interesting conclusions, the fate of the particle under observation is reconstructed from a trio of stereophotographs. Then, in successive order, the curvature caused by the magnet of the bubble chamber, the thickness, length, direction, and angles of the most important lines are measured: detective work from which amazingly precise conclusions can be drawn about the protagonists and the course of events.

Formerly, when a physicist tried to reconstruct phenomena of this type from the photographic records of cosmic rays, it took him on the average an entire day to analyze a single exposure. Later, when the number of photographs increased ten thousand times through the use of accelerators and bubble chambers, and when in addition the exposures contained much more information because of their greater precision, it became necessary to in-

* Any perceptible subatomic process is called an event.

vent instruments to facilitate scanning and partly to automate the measuring process. But even with these aids, five physicists and about fifteen scanning girls worked for about a year to interpret a single experiment. In order to speed up the process, the "Hough-Powell Digitizer" was proposed. It was based on suggestions of Paul Hough of the United States and Brian Powell of Britain, both working at CERN at the time, with the considerable help of Lew Kowarski, head of Data Handling. It is an electronic scanning device which was later improved in close cooperation with the Berkeley and Brookhaven laboratories. The instrument is coupled to a specially programmed computer and requires about twenty seconds at most to find a complex subnuclear event, to analyze it, and to express it numerically. During this time several million multiplications and divisions are performed until the correct result has been selected from an enormous number of possibilities.

The introduction of computers will make it possible to obtain an incomparably greater number of subnuclear events for statistical analysis. The same experiment, for which, in 1960, ten thousand pieces of data were collected with the existing "old" scanning methods, was repeated five years later at Columbia University (New York). Through the use of the computer, in ten days ten million events could be observed, understood, and compared! And one gets a much better idea of the rules and exceptions to the rules in the universe of the smallest dimensions.

"Fortunately, the techniques have not yet reached the stage where we have to get rid of our scanning girls," said one member of the Track Chamber Division, as he led me through the darkened rooms of the Data Handling section, in which the scanners sat before weakly illuminated glass screens and studied the photographs. "But all these processes will sooner or later be almost completely automated. Otherwise we would not be able to handle the flood of information we anticipate. Then another human element will be removed from our production process. What started out as adventure has become automation."

TWO

The Europeans

I

On the premises of CERN, in the midst of large, modern workshops and office buildings, I discovered a weatherbeaten, dirty-gray wooden shack.

"That's Adams Hall," I was told. "It was the headquarters of J. B. Adams and his Proton Synchrotron Group while the Big Machine was being built."

The Englishman John Adams is the personification of CERN's "heroic period," the years when physicists and engineers could feel like pioneers, ready to make all kinds of personal sacrifices to achieve their goal of constructing the world's largest physics research instrument.

When I finally got to meet this almost legendary hero in CERN's history, I was amazed at his youth. In the manner in which he sat opposite me, calm, serene, sure of himself and the rest of the world, Adams did not come across as a historical figure, but rather as someone who still had the peak of his career ahead of him. He is a busy public servant, serving his country in a high official capacity as well as on national and international commissions. In an open-necked sport shirt, tanned, and in high spirits, he looked more like a tennis champion who had just won another match.

"Sometimes I ask myself whether I should write a novel about the building of the Big Machine," he said. "If I only had more time! I even have a title for it: *The Project*. The book would deal with the history of a large technical enterprise in our epoch, a time which is criticized, unjustly in my opinion, for not having produced anything of importance. Naturally, I would describe the technical achievements, but I would mainly describe the people who carry them through, sometimes without knowing whether their work will ever lead to anything. You see, most of us who came to Geneva in 1953 and 1954 took a risk. We had jobs with clear, definite chances of advancement, and exchanged them for complete insecurity. At that time, CERN was no more than a temporary organization, not fully recognized, functioning at its own risk, supported only by the confidence of its 'fathers.' Therefore we were given only short-term contracts that could be canceled at a moment's notice. We had no housing, no proper work space, not even regular medical insurance. When Frank Goward, my predecessor as head of the PS construction group, suddenly could not go on—he showed the first symptoms of the disease of which he died a few months later—he had to rely completely on the charity of his friends. Why did we take those risks? I believe that it was, more than anything, because the war was still with us. We wanted to show that from now on things could be different. The idea that the Dutch, French, Scandinavians, Italians, Swiss, Belgians, Germans, and British would build something together, something that would belong to all of them, to Europe—that was what gripped us."

II

Not long after this encounter with Adams, I saw some documentary photographs of the early days of CERN: Adams Hall covered with icicles—in the terrible winter of 1956. Construction shacks at the edge of the airfield at Cointrin, with young people bent over blueprints. Foundations submerged, or protruding through soft wet earth. An ox being roasted over a large open fire. There was even an amateur color film of those years. I saw it at the home of the famous Italian physicist Edoardo Amaldi in Rome: a group of people bundled up in heavy coats moving rapidly across a flickering, jerking picture. Much too rapidly for me, for I would have liked to pick out their individual faces.

"That one over there . . . that's Francis Perrin. Or is it Pierre Auger? I believe it was after the Uppsala meeting," came a voice out of the darkness.

"Oh no, that looks more like Amsterdam."

"It was at Meyrin . . . *Ecco!* Inspection of the building site after the session of the Conseil. The one with the hat is Niels Bohr."

"And the woman, the small one in black? If only I could remember her name. Mademoiselle Cassigneul, maybe?"

The bunch of prominent people up there on the screen hurried, with staccato movements, through a supermodern landscape of debris. They ran with the speed of villains in an old Chaplin comedy. Attention: wires, wires, and wires once again. A concrete mixer. A metal scaffolding. A dark shaft.

"The tunnel of the Big Machine. That must have been in fifty-six or fifty-seven."

"Edoardo, it's going too fast!"

Someone makes a face at the camera, a few trees shed autumn-colored leaves, a leaning church tower rises up from a worm's eye view. Then a pitch-black hole. But this time it is not a tunnel entrance. The torn film whips against metal with a dry sound, the spool unwinds the narrow ribbon onto the floor. "I'd better put the light on," someone says with resignation.

Professor Edoardo Amaldi is one of the top men in his field. CERN's gigantic PS could hardly have been built without him. And without his later expert guidance of an international study group, the plans for a future, larger machine, to be built by the European research center, would probably not have been finished on time. But with small machines like movie cameras and home projectors this learned scholar is not very dexterous. He knows it himself. Nevertheless, he and his wife, Ginestra, had gone to the trouble of showing me their filmed remembrances of the early days of CERN.

In order to understand the origins of this unique organization that, in contrast to most other postwar international institutions, is constantly held up as ideal, I decided to seek out as many of its founders as possible. This visit to Rome was one of the many side trips I had to make, in order to get to know this unknown land of CERN.

When our joint efforts to unravel the film had failed, I asked the Amaldis to tell me about those days when the large research factory at Meyrin was no more than an idea.

"It couldn't have been very long after the end of the war," Signora Amaldi began. "We had been out to dinner with Rabi,* in Trastevere, and the streetcar back to the center of town would not come, as usual. Our visitor from the States casually asked my husband: 'Why don't the Europeans get together and do physics jointly? At home in the States, nine universities have just pooled their resources and finances to build a large accelerator. You ought to try it too.' "

"Was it really that early that we first spoke about those things?" Amaldi asked. "I unfortunately didn't make note of

* Isador I. Rabi, American Nobel Laureate in physics.

it in my diary. I have only the following there: 'During the academic year 1948-49, there were several conversations between Ferretti* and Amaldi about the idea of establishing a European high-energy physics laboratory. Occasionally, Bernardini† took part in the discussions, during visits to Rome. Bernardini was at that time at Columbia University and discussed the matter with Rabi.' "

Similar entries could presumably be found in French, German, British, and American diaries of the same period. The great dream of one world, united, had once more failed to survive the hardships of war. But might it not now become reality, on a smaller scale at least? Europe—that was already an admission of failure, at the time, of any ambitious, far-reaching hopes. And what remained of world concepts that could not be realized then went under the name of "regional laboratories."

The idea of establishing international research centers had been in the air since the end of the war. The great success of the allied weapons centers had proved that teams of scientists and engineers could get along marvelously together in work groups with well-defined goals. In centers such as Los Alamos, strong personalities with different national backgrounds and temperaments had worked together, and that had not led to energy-consuming friction, as had been feared, but to a considerable augmentation of skills.

In a quiet, almost empty room in the League of Nations Library in Geneva, I was given volume after volume of proceedings on the negotiations and resolutions of the United Nations, during the first year after the war, on the subject of "International Laboratories." Although dating from the very recent past, the documents already read as if they were covered with the dust of generations. In the archaic, ceremonial language of international bureaucracy, world-shaking concepts were formu-

---

* Bruno Ferretti, long-time co-worker of Enrico Fermi.
† Gilberto Bernardini, a student of Fermi, from Florence, and a leading experimentalist.

30

lated—but, unfortunately, they could not shake a world that preferred old quarrels to fresh, modern ideas.

There, I read that Henri Laugier, as spokesman for the French delegation before the Economic and Social Council of the United Nations, had proposed, as early as the fall of 1946, the establishment of laboratories under the auspices of—and possibly financed by—the United Nations, because "the joint creative effort of scientists from different nations could contribute, in great measure, to bringing about an international spirit." A commission of experts was thereupon summoned, which asked scientists all over the world whether they were in accord with the idea, and to suggest problems for these international institutions to work on. The result was an interesting collection of constructive projects, imposing "castles in the air" of the various fields of research. However, the builders who would make them materialize could not be found at the time.

But that could not destroy the dreams of the scientists. One of their most underestimated characteristics is this very imagination, which enables some of them to create, from an abundance of chaotic, even contradictory, phenomena, new concepts and new models. In a similar manner, they were trying to introduce into the turmoil of everyday politics constructive schemes that, sooner or later, might become reality.

The physicist Lew Kowarski was just this kind of forward-looking pioneer. He was born in St. Petersburg, but had lived in western Europe for many years. He became the close collaborator of Pierre Joliot-Curie soon after the latter, in January, 1939, had recognized the full significance of uranium fission, discovered by Otto Hahn and Fritz Strassmann shortly before. The Joliot-Halban-Kowarski trio (later joined by Francis Perrin), famous for important work in atomic physics, paid as much attention, from the very beginning, to the possible industrial and military consequences of their discoveries as to their scientific import.

A few years later, the conversations heretofore restricted to a small circle had grown into large-scale political debates. And Kowarski, who, as a refugee in Canada in the intervening time, had made further important contributions to the development of atomic energy, was a member of the French delegation to the United Nations, negotiating with the representatives of the other great powers over future international control of the new force.

"We scientific experts had an extraordinary amount of time in those days," he told me. "I'm sure you know how tough it was to get anywhere, how painfully slowly the negotiations dragged on. There were hour-long, or even day-long interruptions to allow the diplomats to get new instructions from their governments, or to try, in tedious discussions, to come to an agreement on the interpretation or formulation of certain points. But aren't there similar delays in science, when instruments have to be checked or contradictions straightened out?"

Some of the world's leading physicists had been brought in as technical consultants to the politicians, and the simple truth was that they waited around for days with nothing more to do than merely to be available. It was almost to be expected, then, that they would start talking about their work, about the past, the present, and especially the future of their science, which had suddenly come to the attention of the public. In the yellow-tiled corridors and in the windowless fluorescent-lit meeting rooms of the Sperry Gyroscope Factory, a former armaments plant at Lake Success, New York, that served as provisional headquarters for the United Nations, intensive stock-taking began. And in hotel lobbies, cafeterias, or small foreign restaurants in Manhattan, it continued in greater earnest and in more concrete terms. The scientists were very soon in complete agreement on one point: although the war years had produced truly astounding results in atomic science and technology, they had, in reality, not led to more profound, basically new discoveries regarding the structure of matter. How, when, and where could basic research, so long neglected in favor of weapons research, be taken up again and developed further? That was the question that most concerned the atomic experts in the first months and years after the war.

III

The problem was to push on from where everything had stopped because of the war: after having penetrated to the atomic nucleus, the nature and the structure of the particles found there should now be investigated properly. That the structure of nuclear particles was very much more complicated and multifaceted than had been anticipated, was shown in the very first work done shortly after the war by British, Italian, and French physicists, mostly with rather primitive equipment. They exposed especially sensitive photographic plates or film on mountaintops, such as the Testa Grigia in the Abruzzi range, the Pic du Midi, or the Scottish Highlands, or sent the plates and film up above the earth's haze in balloons. They succeeded in obtaining tracks of cosmic rays from outer space, and in photographing, by this basically primitive means, unusual, unknown "subnuclear events." The latter were produced by particles that, in traversing distant galaxies, had attained energies of billions of electron volts, so that in colliding with terrestrial atomic nuclei they could pierce the enormously strong walls of the nuclei, and enable scientists to gain insight into processes never before observed.

For a systematic study of these processes, however, simple experiments no longer sufficed. The fact that collisions of cosmic rays with nuclei occurred quite infrequently, and under conditions that could not be controlled very well, made it difficult to offer definite scientific statements. It is an essential feature of a convincing experiment that, under the same conditions, others can repeat it, confirm it, and perhaps even improve it.

For that reason, it was necessary to produce highly energetic beams in the laboratory, with mechanical devices, that is, with particle accelerators.

The news that came from the American nuclear research center at Berkeley, shortly after the war, supported the scientists in their belief that the construction of larger and larger machines would necessarily reveal completely new vistas. For, the first new accelerator, the 184-inch cyclotron of the University of California (Berkeley), finished in 1947, had produced in quantity, in its very first experiments, an important elementary particle that physicists had been seeking for more than a decade. Cecil Powell had finally succeeded in finding it, in 1947, in experiments with cosmic rays, but only in small quantity. It was the pi-meson (pion for short) that had been predicted by the Japanese physicist Hideki Yukawa in 1935. The new California accelerator made it possible to produce thousands and thousands of pions within a very short time and then to perform all kinds of experiments with them. Leland Haworth, director of Brookhaven National Laboratory for many years, characterized this milestone in nuclear research in the following way: "In 1948, with the observation of the first artificially created pi-mesons, the era of really modern high-energy physics began."

Even more exciting, however, were the reports that during the war Edwin M. McMillan, in Berkeley, and almost simultaneously Vladimir I. Veksler, in the Soviet Union, had succeeded in developing a new principle for accelerators that seemed to make possible the increase of present energies of millions of volts to billions. Preparation for the construction of a synchrotron in the United States and a "synchrophasotron" in the Soviet Union had already reached an advanced stage.

Did that mean that, in the future, only the United States and the Soviet Union would be able to carry out advanced nuclear research? Was there any choice for European physicists intent on working in this borderline field other than to move to those countries in which they could perform experiments with the most highly developed equipment and most powerful machines? An exodus was already under way. Numerous scientists had left, at least temporarily, western or central Europe and its laboratories, libraries, and institutes, hard hit by the war, for well-equipped America, since that was almost the only place where they could find the conditions to carry on their research successfully. A similar migration was taking place in the other half of the world, from the small and medium-sized Eastern nations to the Soviet Union.

These political aspects of science were also debated at the improvised colloquia of the scientists in New York, and it was not only the Europeans who dreaded a development of this nature.

One of the most fervent advocates of American financial aid to research in the Old World was J. Robert Oppenheimer, who was still burdened by the dubious honor of being the "father of the atom bomb." He backed all projects that might contribute to putting science in a better light again and spoke about it to the French diplomat François de Rose during a weekend visit. "We discussed the future of European civilization in great detail at that time," de Rose recalled, when I looked him up years later at his home in Paris, on the faubourg Saint-Honoré. "Oppenheimer was concerned that the research institutes of Europe, the veritable cradle of the natural sciences, might become deserted, just as the sites of ancient civilizations did centuries ago, that the springs that had nourished the spirit of the entire world might run dry. He emphasized that the Americans had to help further a fruitful scientific life in Europe, not only out of pity, but in their own interest. American research could not do without the stimulation, criticism, and intellectual challenge from outside; it depended on fully equal discussion partners on the other side of the Atlantic."

It was then—de Rose thought it was 1947—that Oppenheimer expressed the idea of establishing a supranational European laboratory for nuclear research. It would not, he stressed, be devoted to the further development of atomic energy and nuclear engineering but to pure, application-free, fundamental research. "The bomb was, in fact, no more than a very evil gadget," "Oppie" had said in the course of the conversation. "Now, we should finally be allowed to turn to deeper problems."

IV

The negotiations concerning international control of atomic energy that took place within the framework of the United Nations, during the first years after the war, not only proceeded with great difficulty but also proved unsuccessful in the end. Despite that, they had at least one important secondary effect: for the first time representatives of both the political and the scientific elite of many nations took part in debates of historic significance, and thus paved the way for completely new relations between the two groups.

The customary alienation between governmental officials and "eggheads," which, even during the war, had led to serious misunderstanding, was gradually being replaced by increased mutual appreciation. The invasion of politics into the preserves of science (and in turn, the demand of some scientists to influence political decisions) had given rise at first to great mistrust on both sides, and even worse, to mutual contempt. It was only during the UN sessions, which dragged on for months and years, that the politicians began to appreciate the qualities of the "scientific method," while the scientists began to develop a feeling for the special features of political thought and action.

A political speaker, after having worked with scientific experts for some time, not only learned some elementary atomic physics but began, often without noticing it, to argue in his own field in a manner somewhat different than before. His knowledge of facts became more precise, he dispensed with rhetoric, and he was ready on occasion to relinquish sticking to the letter of the law in favor of mental experimentation. On the other side, the scientists temporarily seated at the conference table realized that—as Kowarski put it—they could put to good use, in their own problems, the diplomats' techniques for negotiation.

Thus, two new professional types were born, which were often not very far apart: the scientifically arguing politician and the politically thinking scientist. They saw clearly how much they depended upon one another and how strongly their cooperation could influence the future.

A statesman who, long ago, had foreseen the advent of the union of politics and science decreed by fate, was the high French official Raoul Dautry. Earlier, in 1940, as Minister of Defense, he had shown confidence in the physicists who pointed to the possibility of an atomic weapon and had supported them fully, in contrast to the officials of other nations. In 1949, he was immediately fired with enthusiasm when Kowarski—one of the three scientists who had reported on the bright and dark possibilities of nuclear fission, nine years earlier—presented him with a memorandum on the need for European cooperation on questions of nuclear research and nuclear energy. It was clear to him, however, that an undertaking of this kind could be successful only if brought to the attention of the appropriate officials through public opinion. Only then could one circumvent the tendency on the part of the government authorities— particularly the military—to maintain maximum security.

Who would have enough influence, though, to get the project off the ground? Dautry did not have to look far. The European movement inspired by Churchill's famous Zurich address urgently needed tasks and goals to capture the imagination and the willingness to act of the mass public. The Secretary of the Mouvement Européen, Duncan Sandys, Churchill's son-in-law, immediately took the matter into his hands: a cultural conference was called for December 9, 1949, in Lausanne, its main topic to be the state of European research. The high point of the meeting was the reading of a message from Louis de Broglie, the originator of wave mechanics, in which he proposed the establishment of "an international research institution equipped on a financial scale beyond the individual means of the potential member states." Dautry insisted on reading the manifesto himself. It is believed that it was on his advice that the term "atomic research" was never mentioned, because of its unpleasant connotations in the mind of the public.

Even more successful than this first advance toward the public by the "scientific politician," Dautry, was the fact that he won over to his idea of a European laboratory a politically thinking scientist with great skill in diplomacy: Professor Pierre V. Auger, a physicist who had exhibited exceptional ability as a statesman of science in the position of director of higher education of France, and later as head of the Département des Sciences Exactes et Naturelles. Auger climbed still higher in the ranks of scientific politics, and, at the beginning of the 1960's, became head of ESRO (European Space Research Organization). I found a letter in his file in which Dautry had informed him of his plans, and asked for cooperation. There were actually two letters, with identical contents. Dautry was in the habit of sending, out of politeness, one letter handwritten on elegant notepaper and a second typewritten for greater legibility.

Auger resembled his fellow countryman Cardinal Richelieu not only outwardly; he developed unusual skill, in the months and years to come, in his endeavors to bring about a European Laboratory for Nuclear Research. He managed to sail safely past the dangerous reef on which other postwar projects had been wrecked: the interest, too little in finance and too much in politics, usually displayed by the members of the United Nations in connection with such projects. Little by little Auger managed to raise larger and larger sums for the projected European "lab," as it was now called, without granting the supporters a strong voice or even the right of veto. The legal basis for his actions had been carved out for him by another politically oriented scientist, the great American physicist I. I. Rabi, in the almost unanimously adopted resolution of the Fifth General Assembly of UNESCO in Florence, number 2.21, dealing with the necessity for regional neighbor states to cooperate in the establishment of common research centers. Rabi had succeeded in pushing this resolution through over two serious obstacles: the distrust of the members of the American delegation for certain leading European scientists (Joliot-Curie, for example) for political reasons, and the anti-Americanism of many UNESCO member countries.

Almost fifteen years later, this white-haired physicist, still active, told me, on the terrace of a restaurant in Geneva, over the street noises of regained European prosperity, how he had actually accomplished his masterstroke. "I've always known that sometimes it's best to be silent if you want to get something in politics. During the crossing to Europe I promised the other delegates that I would hold my tongue when they presented motions for financial aid, from UNESCO, to cultural institutions in the German Federal Republic. I personally did not approve of these motions; I considered them premature. In return, the other delegates agreed to support my motion for the 'Establishment and Organization of Regional Research Centers and Laboratories.' In Florence, also, I talked as little as possible. I got several European friends to speak to the delegates of other countries about the plan for the laboratory, and to campaign for their votes. By going about it that way, there was less suspicion that my proposal was simply to further American interests. Ultimately, I avoided talking about nuclear research altogether. My motion stated only in very general terms that the international cooperation of scientists, in their search for new knowledge, should be intensified in those fields . . . where the efforts of a single country of the region would not be enough for the particular problem."

When Rabi finally took the floor in the Green Room of the Palazzo Vecchio on June 7, 1950, he knew in advance that it was "in the bag." He had prepared his motion with as much care as he had devoted to his famous experiments, and therefore it was approved by a large majority easily, almost too easily.

Perhaps it was the speed of the voting process that resulted in the public's hardly considering—more, completely overlooking—the possible significance of Resolution 2.21. I searched in vain through back numbers of the largest local newspaper in Florence, *La Nazione*, for a single mention of the resolution, which later was to assume historic proportions. The details of the UNESCO meeting as reported there read like communiqués from the front lines of a major battle in the cold war, the combat lasting days. The delegate from Nationalist China quoted "Dante, the greatest Florentine," and thundered at the representatives from the Communist People's Republics that they belonged "in that circle of hell reserved for the traitors and the soulless"; the Arab delegates launched fierce attacks on Israel; the Czechs and Hungarians left the scene of battle in a rage; and, finally, the Director-General of UNESCO brought into action the big gun, his threat to resign. Attack and counterattack, intrigue and conspiracy, seemed to be in complete command of the scene.

The same tone was also to be found in the final summaries of the world press. Barely five years after World War II, it was stated with resignation that not even within the framework of an organization for the advancement of education, culture and science could positive work among the wartime allies be achieved. And only eight days after the close of the conference, the vision of hell's fires, conjured up in Florence, became horrible reality. Human beings were really writhing in blazing fire: the Korean War had begun with border incidents on the 38th parallel.

V

The political conditions under which the "European Laboratory" left the realm of dreams and plans to enter reality were extremely poor, the financial conditions miserable. The means granted by UNESCO could, at best, be deemed symbolic. The $4,600 pledged could hardly buy a Cadillac, even in 1950. And even this minimal sum was not available immediately. Bookkeeping made it take more than a year for the sums promised by the General Assembly of UNESCO to be forthcoming.

The first actual cash for what was to become CERN came from the pocket of a full-bearded, easily enthused Italian scholar named Gustavo Colonnetti. In his capacity of President of the Italian Research Council, but ultimately completely on his own responsibility, in December, 1950, at the second cultural conference of the European movement in Geneva, he spontaneously pledged some ten thousand lire for the projected European laboratory. Whereupon the French scientists felt that they should contribute a like sum, at least, and the Belgians, in turn, could not let it rest there. Result: at the beginning of 1951, Pierre Auger had sufficient means at his disposal to establish in Paris, the seat of UNESCO, a small "technical bureau" for the planned laboratory, staffed by an administrative coordinator (Jean Mussard) and a scientific expert (Pierre Regenstreif).

At this conference in Geneva, toward the end of 1950, incidentally, it was admitted openly for the first time that nuclear research would be carried out in the planned European Institute. Auger had to try to win over to his project, not only the politicians, but the physicists as well. He was supported primarily by Amaldi, who was associated with the main international organization of physicists, IUPAP (International Union of Pure and Applied Physics). "That was the beginning of my traveling salesman period; my stock: European laboratory," Auger told me, in his office in a forbidding rue Lapérouse mansion, when I asked about CERN's prehistoric period. "And it was a more difficult occupation than I had anticipated."

In the autumn of 1950, at a public event in Oxford, Auger had discovered, to his dismay, that the idea of a supranational research center did not at all meet with the general approval he had expected from scientists. In fact, there was obvious

41

resistance. And soon counterefforts were being made to cause the entire plan to fail. The critical arguments and questions aimed at Auger were almost the same everywhere: "Does it make any sense to build a costly supranational laboratory while our own internal research establishments are so poorly equipped?"

Or: "Would that kind of an organization not lead to an international bureaucracy telling us what we have to work on in our laboratories?"

Finally: "Is it not possible that there is a selfish motive in the political initiative of the Americans, who aim to exploit European scientific talent still more in this way?"

Traveling from capital to capital, from university to university, from congress to congress, Auger tried to refute these objections. He held private conversations, and hour-long round-table discussions with small groups, or addressed audiences of several hundred. Research, he argued, was at the threshold of development: the necessarily expensive technology for experiment made compulsory the sharing of costs and the building of supranational centers. The projected European Laboratory for Nuclear Research was the first important step into new scientific and political territory.

National resistance was shown mainly by the British and the Scandinavians, who were already engaged in building their own small or medium-sized atom smashers. Difficulties arose more often, however, from highly personal sources. A number of heads of institutes and university professors feared that the small "empires" that they had built, with great effort, would be overshadowed by the planned larger international institutions, and might diminish in importance, perhaps even disappear altogether, for lack of funds.

Despite the opposition, the planning office in Paris little by little secured the support of several eminent physicists willing to cooperate, on a personal basis, in the development of plans for the new research center. Kowarski, so active in the early history of CERN, emphasized that the way in which Auger and Amaldi chose to proceed was quite unusual. With all the other more or less successful—sometimes even unsuccessful—attempts to create new international organizations, the procedure had been entirely different. If a new project was to be realized, the governments would first be informed of the plan and invited to send representatives. When these officially appointed delegates convened, they were obliged, of necessity, to speak as directed by their governments. It was therefore not seldom that they were compelled to defend an opinion they did not share from the very beginning, or did no longer hold after having discussed it with colleagues from other countries. In the case of the European laboratory, the procedure was the other way round: this time it was not the governments that were first asked to cooperate, but the scientists of the countries concerned. Presumably, they would then influence their governmental authorities, instead of being selected by them and bound by irrelevant directives.

It now turned out to be fortunate that UNESCO had granted such a pitiful sum for the project, and that the early costs had been covered to so small an extent by the budget of the world organization. Therefore Auger could risk choosing such an unusual procedure regardless of the right of five dozen member states to be heard. In retrospect, it proved to be a further stroke of luck that a plan by Rabi, that seemed very good at the time, could not be put into effect. The plan called for using the Marshall Plan "Counterpart Funds," accumulated in France, to finance the first stages of the international laboratory. The elimination of Rabi's plan meant that the Americans would now not be able to exert financial influence on the further development of the project.

On April 26, 1951, things were so far advanced that Auger, Amaldi, and the two members of the UNESCO planning office were able to compose a list of scientific experts, who would prepare a first draft of possible future problems, and expected costs, of the laboratory. With that, the prehistory of CERN entered a second phase. Four weeks later, on May 23, nine physicists from eight nations (H. Alfvén, Sweden; E. Amaldi, Italy; E. Capron, Belgium; O. Dahl, Norway; F. Goward, United Kingdom; F. A. Heyn, Netherlands; L. Kowarski and F. Perrin, France; P. Preiswerk, Switzerland) joined Auger, in Paris, at the first "meeting of experts." The group was intentionally kept small, in order to be accommodated easily at one of the conference tables in the somewhat run-down salon of the former Hôtel Majestic, or at a dining table in the Auberge du Coucou.

The experts worked out a program, in only a few days, outlining the dimensions of the proposed accelerator, and the size of the staff and the budget for the laboratory. But the most important idea to emerge from the deliberations was that the founding of the research center should proceed in steps. Before anything else, toward the end of the year, the European member states of UNESCO—each represented by one diplomat and one scientist—should convene at a higher level. (The conference would also include those members who, up to now, had not been represented on the commission of experts—West Germany, for example.) The first act of this panel would be to form a "provisional organization," supported by a budget of approximately $240,000, whose only purpose would be to formulate, as exactly as possible, within twelve to eighteen months, a scientific, technological, and financial seven-year plan for the large project.

Kowarski, one of the French representatives at this meeting of the "ten wise men," explained: "The experts had the feeling —and later events proved them right—that a provisional organization, with its relatively small budget, would of necessity exert an encouraging influence. It would bring together the governmental representatives, would facilitate a gradual mutual adjustment of differences, and finally would bring about, almost unnoticeably, the transition to greater commitment and firmer relations."

The fact that CERN went through a carefully planned trial period supposedly was one of the reasons for the later unusual success of the institution. Thus, a detailed description of the prehistory of the research institute seems warranted. For here is an example of the gradual growth of an international organization, which could serve as a model for similar projects.

Some referred to these tactics as an "engagement period," which permits the partners to get to know one another better before taking the final marriage vows. But would it not be more suitable to compare it to the way scientific and technological work is done in development laboratories, where the prototype of a new machine does not spring forth, in final form, from the brain of a single designer, but is drafted, and redrafted, examined, changed, and re-examined, step by step in test after test? Here, probably for the first time in history, an international organization was brought to maturity experimentally, like a modern technical device, before it was actually put to work.

VI

During December of 1951, a few hours before the opening of the large official conference on the planned European Laboratory for Nuclear Research, for which politicians and scientists (including four Nobel Laureates) of twelve nations had already registered, the Director-General of UNESCO, Sr. Jaime Torres-Bodet of Mexico, supposedly had second thoughts about the dimensions of the undertaking.

The following dialogue was held at that time (and verified personally by one of the two participants) between the head of the world organization and his right-hand man and later successor, René Maheu.

Torres-Bodet (after glancing over the estimates): "Do I understand this correctly? Fifty *million* dollars for a single research institute?"

Maheu (slightly sarcastically): "That is correct, Mr. Director-General, and that is only the beginning. I estimate that the final cost of the project will be ten times that amount."

Torres-Bodet: "Sheer idiocy! It is impossible!"

In those days such a negative prognosis was not as absurd as it seems today. The Korean incident of June, 1950, had become a full-scale war by then, and most of the member states of UNESCO were feeling the burden of defense spending, which increased from month to month. The end of the armed engagement was yet not in sight, and, in fact, people feared that the local friction might spread into a world conflagration. Was it not unrealistic, then, to ask the governments for an eight-figure sum for the advancement of science, and not even research that gave promise of military or commercial application, but pure science?

Probably the scientists were not as unrealistic as they appeared, however. One of the "fathers" of CERN, who shall remain nameless for obvious reasons, winked slyly as he gave me his version of the calculated act put on by his colleagues, unjustly labeled naïve:

"What was the general feeling toward science in the years after the war? Politicians and economists had learned from experience that work in the natural sciences, even when it seemed far out and abstruse, could under certain conditions have revolutionary practical consequences. That was especially true of the field they called atomic research. Therefore they hoped that nuclear physics would, sooner or later, produce something tangible for them, just as atomic physics had, earlier. A super-source of power, perhaps, or a superweapon. In any event, one had to keep up with this undertaking, in order not to be left behind again. We did not especially encourage this widespread speculation among the laymen in high political positions, nor did we especially discourage it either, for we knew it would serve our purpose ultimately."

Was it right, though, to build on such false expectations on the part of the governments? Would not the ethical foundation of research suffer if, out of opportunism, political support was accepted, and with it political ties? There were some scientists —the "Copenhagen group" around Niels Bohr and Professor Hans Kramers of Holland, in particular, at that time—who were doubtful about the procedure. Furthermore, it seemed to them that the proposals for the European laboratory, formulated in Paris, were too grandiose, too presumptuous. Some saw in it an expression of the hubris that, since Hiroshima, had possessed some of the physicists in the spotlight of public attention.

Nowhere had I read anything about these objections to the first plans for CERN; they had come to me in the form of hints from Auger. Was there any written documentation? Presumably not any longer, thought Jean Mussard, for the records in which the objections of the Copenhagen group could have been found had been discarded by UNESCO, together with other dispensable documents dated earlier than 1956, in a general clearance of its files.

I found the information quite depressing. It was not the first time I had been met with the disappearance of sources of the history of science, because of lack of interest. Scientists ordinarily exhibit little feeling for history, and make no effort to preserve their personal records. My imagination conjured up visions of fierce "paper wolves" lurking in the basements of UNESCO and all the other large organizations, waiting to tear to shreds all the letters, memoranda, and plans of the early days of the world's first supranational laboratory. A few days later, I paid a visit to a lady of the editorial staff of *Impact*. She led me, with a smile, into a neighboring office. There on a desk lay huge, half-untied bundles of memoranda, minutes, letters, and newspaper clippings: the documents of the "Technical Bureau," the nucleus of CERN. For once, praised be the slowness of bureaucracy! Thanks to it, this treasure had not been transformed into refuse long ago.

An examination of this extensive source material, preserved for a time from the fate of the other papers, would be a fascinating study in itself. Here, we will limit ourselves to stating that the most serious crises that threatened the creation of CERN from time to time did not stem from differences among the individual nations nor from differences between the scientists and the politicians, but from lack of agreement among the physicists themselves. Personal motivations and individual likes and dislikes had a considerable part in the conflict. But basically it was a matter of principle. The group around Niels Bohr felt that nuclear research was on the verge of entering an entirely new era, in which not only its means of support and its dimensions, but its dependence and its vulnerability as well, had to grow continually. They cautioned over and over that the traditional academic style of research had to be maintained in the transition. The views of the Copenhagen group regarding the most appropriate measures to intensify European cooperation in nuclear research were so different, at first, from the views of the staunch supporters of CERN, that not one of the former was represented at the extremely important conference of experts, in May, 1951. After Nazism had ruined the prestige of Göttingen, and the death of Rutherford had dimmed the aura of Cambridge, Bohr's institute was looked upon as the spiritual center of European nuclear research, a fact that was not properly recognized, according to its members, by the Paris Bureau and the international group of experts. It seemed at the time that the opposing views could not be reconciled. This was manifest, on the Copenhagen side, in an unusually strong letter Professor Kramers addressed to UNESCO, and on the other side, in a rather derogatory report, by the Paris experts, on the alleged technical backwardness of the Bohr Institute; although the report had not been published, its contents were common knowledge.

But in this instance, and others later, the physicists demonstrated their ability to iron out differences in an objective, friendly manner. Intensive discussion made the two opposing views come closer and closer together. The arguments of the Copenhagen group were taken into consideration, to a large extent, in establishing, provisionally, a "Division of Theoretical Physics" in the Danish capital (as part of the European laboratory), as well as in deciding to build, next to the Big Machine, the "smaller machine" (the synchro-cyclotron) that had entered into the discussions earlier. In February, 1952, Bohr attended the second intergovernmental meeting of the founders of CERN. In May of the same year, this scholar, revered by many scientists as a father figure, was appointed to the Executive Council of the provisional organization, where he participated wholeheartedly from then on in the development of the research institute. Weisskopf reminisced later, in a memorial address in honor of the great scientist, about how the aged Bohr once, after a day-long session, managed to find time to stroll through rainy Geneva for hours with another Council member, in order to discuss some points that were not quite clear.

Then the scientists got their first taste of the conflicts that lay in store for them with their sponsors, the politicians. In December, 1951, when the physicists for the first time met, not among themselves, but with the political delegates of their supporting governments, with François de Rose as chairman, an unpleasant incident occurred. The representative of the Italian Foreign Ministry refused to recognize Amaldi as the second representative of his country, and requested that the professor be excluded from the meeting for being too far to the left for the Italian's governmental taste.

This demand created a truly bizarre situation, for it was Amaldi who was credited, together with Rabi, Dautry, Auger, and Kowarski, with being one of the first and most ardent supporters of the laboratory, the realization of which was the very purpose of the meeting. But this argument could not convince his fellow countryman, politically oriented in another direction. He threatened to leave immediately. In order to keep the conference from disintegrating, Amaldi decided to be absent from the founding session of "provisional CERN." Later, it became possible to make the "cold warrior" relax his stand. On December 18, Amaldi was able to take his well-deserved seat at the conference table. Before the talks began that morning, Sir George Thomson, present as the British observer, crossed the entire room ostentatiously to shake Amaldi's hand and simultaneously turn his back on the political disturber of the peace sitting next to him.

There were no similar incidents in later sessions of the CERN Council. Each member state sent two delegates. In most cases one was a prominent government official and the other a distinguished scientist. The combination proved an effective team.

Political tensions at the first official founding conference could be felt, indirectly, in another way: the Communist member states of UNESCO that had been invited to take part in the conference did not send representatives—did not reply at all, in fact. In their eyes the proposed European laboratory was an "American establishment" that they later attacked in newspapers, meetings, and parliamentary discussions.

VII

CREEPLIOAFCRN*—not a chemical formula, not a secret code, but the original, somewhat clumsy designation formed from first letters, that was later contracted to CERN—was in use for the short period between February 15 and June of 1952. Auger then proposed the shorter CERN. The first stationery bearing CERN on its letterhead was ordered in July, 1952, and has hardly been changed since.

The administrative structure of the organization could not be simplified as easily as could its name. The organization entered its third phase in May, 1952. Its structure was almost ad-

---

* Conseil des Representants d'Etats Européens pour l'Etude des Plans d'un Laboratoire International et l'Organisation d'Autres Formes de Cooperation dans la Recherche Nucléaire (Council of Representatives of European States for the Study of Plans for an International Laboratory and the Organization of Other Forms of Cooperation in Nuclear Research).

venturously intricate and inefficient, in its provisional state. Under an international Council of Representatives (composed of two representatives from each government) coordinated with a Scientific Policy Committee, was the actual apparatus for working out the plans for the laboratory. It consisted of a Secretariat-General headed by Amaldi, and four work groups: the Theoretical Division under Bohr, the Proton Synchrotron Group under Dahl, the Synchro-Cyclotron Group under Bakker, and the Laboratory Group under Kowarski. The functioning of the organization was, above all, complicated by the fact that the new research center temporarily had no single location. The leading figures carried out their duties from their home bases, and, in most cases, it was in addition to other teaching or research responsibilities. The Secretary-General was in Rome, the Theoretical Study Group in Copenhagen, the division responsible for the plans of the smaller machine (the synchro-cyclotron) was in Amsterdam, while Odd Dahl, the designer of the large accelerator (called "cosmotron" at that time), had his headquarters in the Norwegian port of Bergen, and his right-hand man, Frank Goward, spent most of his time in England, at Harwell. The Laboratory Group, in charge of the future site, design, and administrative structure of the research center, was directed by Kowarski, mainly from Paris, and his assistant, Paul Preiswerk, from Zurich, and would arrange to meet in still other cities on the continent (in Brussels, for example). If one were to add to the five senior officers the two vice-directors of CREEPLIOAFCRN, the leading administrators of the growing laboratory resided in no fewer than seven different European countries.

The legal agreement for "provisional CERN" was signed on February 15, 1952, by eleven nations, the signatures appearing in the following order: Federal Republic of Germany, Denmark, France, Greece, Italy, the Netherlands, Sweden, Switzerland, Yugoslavia, Belgium, Norway. The United Kingdom temporarily delegated only an observer.

51

The following telegram was sent to I. I. Rabi that day: "We have just signed the agreement, the official birth certificate of the child you created in Florence."

Beginning with May 5, 1952, the scattered provisional organization was governed by Edoardo Amaldi, who immediately paid for the honor of the appointment with a new raincoat which, in his excitement, he left somewhere, in accordance with the image of the absent-minded professor.

Amaldi showed no absent-mindedness in his ruling of the large empire. He directed its fate with firmness, from rooms in the Istituto di Fisica, or from the cooler basement of the building during the summer months. There, through the routine of daily activity, the first cell of "Pan-Europe" grew, the Pan-Europe that Count Richard Coudenhove-Kalergi had called for as early as the end of World War I, and for which he had been unjustly labeled a dreamer by the people of his time.

The problem was to coordinate the work of Rome with that of the CERN groups scattered over an entire continent, the headquarters of UNESCO, and numerous university institutes, as though all were located in a single country. Thus, a net was woven tighter and tighter in the Eternal City, that extended from Liverpool to Uppsala, from Copenhagen to Cagliari, from Freiburg and Brussels to Dublin and Zurich, from Delft to Grenoble, from Harwell to Paris and Padua. And national borders gradually faded behind the criss-crossings.

VIII

After the end of World War II, editorials, speeches, and textbooks claimed that a new breed of people began to develop— Europeans. Such wishful thinking had become reality in a natural way for the still-small staff of "provisional CERN." These "first Europeans" did not look upon themselves as couriers on a historic mission, but they began, almost unconsciously, to talk, write, even dream in three or four languages. Their favorite walks, shops, restaurants, coffeehouses, theaters, and bars were in ten or twelve different countries, their friends were scattered over an entire continent. The expanded environment did not seem foreign to them; it was incorporated into their own personal sphere.

Eliane Bertrand, the vivacious head secretary, for example, thought it quite natural that her clothes, her books, and the rest of her possessions should be distributed over half of Europe. In the haste of a necessary trip to another European city, there was often no time for packing. One had to rush directly from office to airport. It was a good idea, therefore, to have one's most indispensable personal items ready for use at several strategic points in Europe.

A charming expression of the burgeoning European mentality is to be found in the long, handwritten letters, in UNESCO's files, that were sent from Rome to the Paris office by Marie-Simone, one of Amaldi's secretaries. Interspersed with official matters is amusing continental patter on the weather, clothes, medicine, rent, menus, and different modes of life. Europe had suddenly become one big hotel, with varied but familiar noises, odors, and rumors.

These Europeans had rapidly become accustomed to foreign languages, different national customs, and sudden changes in climate. They found it difficult to adjust, however, to the stringent regulations of international bureaucracy imposed upon them as members of an official supranational organization. There were precise instructions on how to write letters, prepare reports, charge expenses, or make financial estimates.

"Every one of our members, each from a different country, thought his way of bookkeeping was the only right way," recalled CERN's head of finance, Tièche of Switzerland, "and that, naturally, caused problems, at first." Tièche had been snatched from a position of responsibility in Berne, in the "Amaldi era," to put Helvetic order into CREEPLIOAFCRN's financial confusion. "At the very moment of his arrival he sensed that the organization with which he was dealing was somewhat unorthodox. He was met at the station, not with an automobile but with a motor scooter. Caroline De Mol, the most cheerful of the Istituto di Fisica's secretaries, without comment invited the visitor to take his place on the rear of her small Lambretta, and off they roared at breakneck speed to headquarters. When he managed to catch his breath, the newcomer shouted into the ear of his chauffeur that, although she drove somewhat rapidly, she drove quite well.

"Mille grazie!" she shouted back, "I've only been at it a week!"

Later, this expert was left with a pile of receipts (some scribbled in pencil) from all over Europe, in the illusory hope that he would soon bring order to the chaos. Earlier, a chartered accountant from the world-renowned firm of Price, Waterhouse & Company had torn his hair out over the task. When the books had been laid in front of the mild-mannered gentleman, dressed in typically English conservative fashion, he took one brief look at them, and made the following formal pronouncement: "I have had quite a bit of experience. I have examined books even in darkest Africa. But upon my word, this is worse than anything I encountered from the natives! And I was under the impression that this was a scientific undertaking."

Despite the mess, or perhaps because the new European organization was still tinged with adventurousness and Bohemianism—the main agreement between CERN and UNESCO was kept in a cookie tin, for example—because nothing had become rigid through routine, because one acted less according to the "Handbook for International Organizations" than according to one's own feeling and judgment, because everyone in this small international group knew everyone else, because people were united not by regulations but by enthusiasm, not by contracts but by friendships—because of all that, even after many years, people still went into raptures over the happy days when they and Europe were still young.

IX

Four cities fought for the honor of harboring the European institute for nuclear research. Apart from Geneva and Copenhagen, both of which had expressed interest as early as 1951, Paris and Arnhem campaigned vigorously. Rivalries of this nature always crop up when smaller units join to form a larger entity. The contest is then decided, most assuredly, not by objective arguments but on the basis of power and influence.

It was thought that the selection of the "atomic capital of Europe," as the future seat of CERN was termed in the newspapers, should be handled in an entirely different way, however. The most appropriate place should be determined strictly scientifically, in the most objective manner. With that in mind, the group under Kowarski and Preiswerk, responsible for the design and building of the laboratory, sent a list of twenty-two questions to the interested governments. The list took account of all possible concerns, ranging from the nature of the soil and the need for unusually large amounts of power and water to the accommodation of personnel, schooling, and shopping.

The replies served only to increase the torment of selection. The material conditions for the laboratory seemed to be pretty much the same everywhere, according to the numerous applications received at the beginning. Kowarski attempted, therefore, to find some other objective criteria by which to make the best selection. For example, he calculated which spot on the map of Europe was equidistant from the scientific centers of the member states. Assuming that the United Kingdom would eventually join CERN, he found a point near Karlsruhe that most closely met the requirement. But a German city was impossible, seven years after the war, for political reasons. Psychological factors also had to be considered, and these could not be measured with a ruler.

Should the tranquillity necessary for intensive intellectual

55

work, which the Dutch promised in their response to the questionnaire, or the advantages of a cosmopolitan city with a rich cultural life, which the Danes boasted of Copenhagen, be decisive factors? Would it be easier in Geneva, or in Paris, for a foreign member of CERN to adjust to strange surroundings?

"Housing conditions, as well as the cultural atmosphere, . . . and educational and recreational facilities, determine, to a great extent, the ability to work and the creative potential of the staff members," Kowarski remarked, in his report on the attempts to find a site, and added, for the benefit of those who considered human factors of secondary importance: "The best technical equipment can soon be ruined, when operated by someone in a bad mood."

The decision regarding the site of the European research institute was scheduled for the third meeting of the provisional organization, to be held in Amsterdam at the beginning of October, 1952. At that time it seemed a certainty that, of the four cities in the final running, neither Paris (because of its size, its high cost of living, and the threat of strikes that might cause delays in construction) nor Copenhagen (because of unyielding opposition on the part of the French) stood a chance. Only Arnhem and Geneva remained.

It proved to be of decisive importance that Geneva had, in Councilor of State Albert Picot, a particularly convincing advocate. The former President of the Swiss National Council, together with a number of friends and prominent people, had made strong efforts, since the end of the Second World War, to maintain the position of Geneva, the League of Nations city, as the seat of important international organizations, even after the UN headquarters had been removed to the United States. They succeeded, as much as through purposeful as through generous policy, contrary to the expectations of those who feared that Calvin's city would deteriorate into a provincial Swiss town after the failure of the League of Nations. Fair terms in tax and customs matters, and, above all, the tolerance toward foreign visitors practiced then by the Genevans (but no longer, unfortunately) proved quite effective: in 1952 Geneva was once more a miniature metropolis. Its small size was even considered an advantage, for cosmopolitanism and provincialism met there most pleasantly; imposing office buildings of international agencies and large enterprises bordered quaint, small-town streets and charming, rustic bistros.

The friendly little Dutch city of Arnhem had little to put up against this trump hand. In addition, something unforeseen had an effect. As fate would have it, the reception given by the Arnhem city fathers for the site selection committee of CERN occurred on an extremely rainy day, Picot told me while I was visiting him on Sunday morning at his patrician home in Geneva. "The beautiful bouquets and the lavish banquet didn't help one bit. Only two hotels in town, no university, no international school, only a few foreign newspapers at the station or in bookstores, and on top of that rotten weather—these were too many handicaps to overcome. After this visit I was certain: Geneva would win."

And that is exactly what happened. At the next meeting of CERN's Council of Representatives, Professor Francis Perrin, on behalf of France, withdrew the application of Paris in favor of Geneva; the Danes followed suit, and the Dutch could hardly do other than agree: Geneva was chosen unanimously as the seat of the first European laboratory for nuclear research. The founders of CERN thought they were rid of one worry, at least. But they were wrong.

X

The CERN resolution that Councilor Picot triumphantly carried back to his city in October, 1952, did not please all the Genevans. Considerations involving world politics, and personal fears about radiation released in atomic experiments were brought up, in order to prevent, in the interests of the people, the erecting of the atomic laboratory within the confines of the canton of Geneva. The attacks began at the end of the week in which the news of Geneva's selection reached the public. In an article in Geneva's Communist organ, *Voix Ouvrière,* entitled "The Allegedly 'European' Atomic Institute," Monsieur Ducommun, assistant leader of the Parti du Travail (the Communist party) in the State Council of Geneva, sounded all the notes that were to become the central theme of a public debate heard by the entire world. In the article, the statement was made for the first time that the new institute would become an "agent of the bomb manufacturers." And that immediately led to a second "disclosure": the activities of the researchers in Geneva would benefit the members of the Atlantic Pact, the Americans in particular, for the Soviet Union and the satellite countries had been excluded from this "European" council. In essence, the article stated that a few minutes from Geneva, at Verbois, buildings were being erected which someday might be considered part of America's atomic system.

This attitude on the part of the Communists toward the European laboratory had long been expected. Prior to the publication of the article, officials in the Eastern Bloc and Communist parties in the West had reacted to the project only with silence. But because the Eastern members of UNESCO (the Soviet Union did not belong at the time) had completely ignored the invitation to the first intergovernmental conference in December, 1951, rejection by the Communists could be anticipated.

Then the cold war that, before this, had barely grazed CERN, erupted in full force. The Communist party brought it to the Geneva State Council. During a debate at the beginning of December, one of the councilors, Monsieur Borel, speaking in favor of CERN's coming to Geneva, was shouted down with loud cries of "European spirit, made in U.S.A.!" and "At Eisenhower's command!" The session finally had to be adjourned. But the discussion, a wild melée by then, raged on in the lobby of the local parliament. Some Communists had got into fist fights with conservatives. Only through the intervention of the parliament guards was a veritable riot prevented. "Monsieur Ducommun, shaking, and Monsieur Armand Magnin, purple with rage, shouted at one another incoherently, while Monsieur Monnet was held back by his coattails to prevent something terrible from happening," according to the account in the *Tribune de Genève*.

The Swiss constitution provides for the possibility of initiating a referendum on controversial issues if a certain number of signatures is obtained from among the registered voters. In Geneva, at that time, 5,000 signatures were enough to ensure a plebiscite on a public controversy. For the "CERN issue" over 7,600 signatures were gathered. The citizens were to be brought to the polls to voice their opinion on "the prevention of the establishment of an atomic institute in the Canton of Geneva."

The number was surprisingly large. It was not only the Communists and fellow travelers who had expressed concern over the coming of CERN. Middle-class and even extreme right-wing groups also saw in the planned laboratory a serious danger to their home city. Some were of the opinion that the lives of the people might be endangered, or their health impaired, by atomic radiation or by an accidental atomic explosion. Others held that the experiments to be undertaken might interfere with air traffic, with vegetation, even with television reception. But the argument that had the greatest impact was that the neutrality of Switzerland precluded the establishment of an international laboratory in which not a single Communist country was represented.

Because of the unusual coalition of the extreme left and the conservatives, the outcome of the plebiscite, scheduled for the end of June, 1953, could not be predicted; and in the office of the Secretary-General there was concern that, if the opponents of the research center should emerge victorious, no other country would receive the CERN laboratories.

The struggle for CERN soon became a political issue that aroused interest far beyond the confines of Geneva's local politics. For the first time, atomic questions were not being decided from above, and from behind closed doors, but were being brought before the voting public for open discussion and decision. For several weeks the whole town of Geneva became essentially one large lecture hall. Physicists, chemists, psychologists, political scientists, clergymen, and doctors spoke in convention halls, auditoriums, inns, and gymnasiums on scientific issues which, until then, had never been discussed in such depth and before so wide an audience.

Misconceptions could be set straight in that way, and fears could be allayed. The champions of the laboratory tried above all to remove the demonic connotations from the term "atom," the handwriting on the wall to many. It was by no means true that all atomic research was directed toward the production of new weapons and new sources of power, they explained. The high-energy physics that would be conducted in Geneva would, probably for a long time, have no practical applications whatever. It was not matter that was to be transformed here into energy, as with uranium bombs and piles, but energy into infinitely small masses. The nuclear physicists were not striving for more power but for more knowledge. Therefore all the results of their research would be published immediately. Neutral Switzerland had been selected as the site of the European laboratory primarily because any suspicion that war research was being conducted there would be dissolved.

Were these arguments convincing? People had their doubts when Professor William Rappard, an internationally recognized political scientist and an expert on questions of neutrality, to the astonishment of many of his friends sided with the opponents of CERN. He based his stand on the premise that in case of war

60

the Soviet Union might bomb the research institute it boycotted. Rappard's argument seemed a real danger to the cause, so much so that at the last minute the supporters of CERN procured, from the Swiss government at Berne, an official statement declaring that the laboratory would be closed instantly if war were to break out.

After these bitter exchanges that divided the city into two camps and temporarily broke up lifelong friendships like that of Picot and Rappard, the vote was expected to be extremely close. The actual result was all the more surprising, then. The 7,332 votes garnered by the opposition did not even come up to the original number of signatures for the referendum; those favoring building the laboratory in the canton of Geneva mustered double the amount, 16,539 votes.

While the Genevans were still heading for the polls on June 29, 1953, the sixth CERN Council meeting opened in Paris for the purpose of dissolving "provisional CERN" (established February 15, 1952) by the adoption and signing of a binding agreement, the Convention Permanente. The provisional period had come to an end. It had been demonstrated that the partners could work well together, and now they intended to put their joint plans into practice. Even the United Kingdom, which had participated only as an observer until then, was finally willing to relinquish its attitude of waiting, and also to sign the document. Sir Ben Lockspeiser, the British representative, had contributed a great deal to the earlier discussions on the drafting of a Convention and on the sharing of the first substantial cost (about $30 million).

The formal signing of the document was to take place July 1, 1953, in the Salon de l'Horloge du Quai d'Orsay. Immediately upon learning the favorable outcome of the Geneva referendum, State Councilor Picot took a sleeper to Paris in order to present in person the "triumphant result" of his campaign to the CERN Council. While the Geneva vote had at first been considered by the founders of CERN to be an unforeseen, even annoying, hindrance, its outcome was now greeted with great enthusiasm. The laboratory had received truly democratic acceptance, through extensive public discussion of cultural matters, something that, according to Picot, had not occurred since the days of Athens.

THREE

The
Project

I

Before the European Laboratory for Nuclear Research was built, even before it acquired legal status on paper, the plans for it provided the stimulus for a decisive breakthrough in nuclear engineering.

It occurred in August, 1952. A delegation from the Proton Synchrotron Group (Dahl and Wideroë of Norway and Goward of England) in charge of plans for the construction of CERN's Big Machine intended to visit Brookhaven National Laboratory at Upton, New York, near New York City, where the world's largest particle accelerator, the "cosmotron," was located. Their plan originally was to use, on a larger scale, the design of the Brookhaven machine, which had been in operation only a few months, and accelerated protons to the highest energy attained thus far, three billion electron volts (3 BeV). The instrument projected for CERN was to achieve energies four or five times greater, according to a recent decision of a scientific commission meeting in Copenhagen. Only then could the planned accelerator open up new territories and systematically produce nuclear particles that were either still unknown or that had been predicted theoretically but had not yet been verified experimentally.

When the American physicist Stanley Livingston, a student and co-worker of the great Ernest O. Lawrence (who is associated with the invention of the first circular accelerator, the cyclotron, in 1930), learned of the impending visit of the Europeans, he immediately asked himself whether simply copying the cosmotron was the right thing to do, or was even possible to do.

The history of particle accelerators had shown that a genuine increase in capacity had always gone hand in hand with the introduction of a radically new technological concept. This was how it had been possible to increase the power of the instruments for generating and accelerating nuclear particles to such a great extent within only a quarter of a century. First there were the high-voltage devices of Wideroë and Merle Tuve; then came the accelerators of Sir John Cockcroft and Ernest T. S. Walton, that made use of vacuum tubes; next came the belt generator of Robert Van de Graaff. With the cyclotron, the betatron, the synchro-cyclotron, and now the first proton synchrotron, physicists had succeeded in increasing the energy of the accelerators tenfold every six years, on the average.

This development in steps made it necessary for the magnets to become stronger, larger, and heavier, for their fields, like animal tamers, forced the increasingly energetic particles to travel a circular path and not escape. The weight of the magnets for the 1 BeV accelerator at Birmingham was 810 tons, the total weight of the magnets for the 3 BeV machine at Brookhaven was 1,650 tons, and for the 6 BeV monster at Berkeley, which was to be finished in 1956, plans called for magnets weighing as much at 10,000 tons. According to this progression, for a machine of 10-15 BeV, as was being planned for CERN, magnets with a total weight exceeding 35,000 tons would be required. Livingston did not approve of the idea, because so huge an apparatus would not only be very costly, but it would also be far too unwieldy, in relation to its capacity.

This time, too, it seemed necessary to think of something more original than mere scaling up of a machine already in existence. Might it not be possible to find a new principle for the projected European machine? But which? That was the big question that went through Stanley Livingston's mind time and again after he learned that a CERN delegation was to visit Brookhaven. The physicist whose name suggests the historic encounter of two explorers in Africa (David Livingstone and Henry M. Stanley) made it known that he was about to set out for the virgin territory beyond the 10 BeV border. That is, he withdrew from his usual work in the laboratory, for several days, in order to be able to concentrate. The equipment for his spiritual adventure consisted only of a pencil, paper, and a slide rule.

Soon Ernest Courant and Hartland Snyder came to the aid of the "expedition." Livingston had informed them that he had come up against an insurmountable obstacle. He described the further course of events as follows:

"We found the stumbling block—and it turned out to be made of pure gold."

The find was made through the simple consideration that it might be possible to compress the proton beam, that was to travel in the new machine, to a greater degree than had been done in earlier types of accelerators. Then the aperture of the magnets, which "pinch" the beam of particles traveling in the vacuum chamber, could be made much smaller, and consequently the weight of the magnets themselves (and their cost) could be reduced correspondingly. How might this be achieved? It occurred to the investigators to apply to their problem the principle of "strong-focusing" that had been known in optics for many years. Just as a beam of light that is focused by being sent alternately through convex and concave lenses becomes narrower and brighter, in an accelerator the proton beam that is successively directed through vertical and horizontal magnetic fields might well become more concentrated and gain in intensity.

The first reactions of the experts to the obviously good idea were mixed. For instance, Edwin M. McMillan, the inventor of the synchrotron, found the unorthodox idea fascinating from a theoretical point of view, but he was doubtful whether movements as delicate as those of bunches of protons in an accelerator could be controlled adequately. The concept called for an arrangement whereby elementary particles traveling at very nearly the speed of light were to be shoved along a zigzag path from one magnet to the next, like "drunkards lurching from one side of the street to the other."

The members of the CERN delegation, who had arrived at Brookhaven in the meantime, were immediately drawn into hour-long discussions of the new principle. They took up their American colleagues' idea with enthusiasm. The first crude estimates showed that the saving achieved through the decrease in size of the magnets and of the circular vacuum chamber where the accelerated particles were to circulate, would make it possible to construct, for almost the same sum that had been allotted, an apparatus with twice the original energy (about 30 BeV). The accelerator would then be ten times as powerful as the largest machine in existence at the time, Brookhaven's cosmotron! The delegates from CERN were convinced that this project, embodying a completely new principle, by all means had to be put to the test, even if it meant abandoning all the construction plans that had already been drafted and starting all over again from the beginning.

II

It proved to be especially fortunate that the preparatory work for the Big Machine had been entrusted to a man who, friends and students maintained, hated nothing worse than routine and boredom. All his life, Norway's Odd Dahl had managed to avoid the two. As a young mechanic he had worked toward a pilot's license in his spare time, when flying was still hazardous, in order to be able to accompany his fellow countryman Roald Amundsen on a two-year polar expedition. Upon the conclusion of that adventure he bumped along caravan routes in central Asia in an old jalopy to carry out investigations on geomagnetism; he climbed the highest peaks in the Andes after cosmic rays; rode unexplored rapids of the Amazon in a small boat as a missionary's assistant; and finally, in 1930, built, at the Carnegie Institute in Washington, with Tuve, one of the first primitive particle accelerators, from a Tesla coil and a long, humpbacked glass tube.

Dahl had been recommended by Edoardo Amaldi for his position at CERN. The first Secretary-General had been told about the "mad Viking" several times, during a visit to Washington. He began to show serious interest in the Norwegian when he saw with his own eyes the excellent apparatus that Dahl had built in the capital before his wanderlust had drawn him on.

"What impressed me more than his marvelous instruments," Amaldi said, "was the spirit he had left behind with his co-workers, the joy in the scientific adventure, the mixture of realism, enthusiasm, and optimism with which they took up something new. That was exactly what we needed for our laboratory. So I started out to look for Dahl. I finally traced him where I least expected: at home in Bergen, Norway. He had been given an entire institute there. In spite of that it wasn't hard to talk him into helping us, at least for as long as our work was still in its initial stages."

One can imagine how enthusiastic Dahl was about the unexpected alteration in the construction plans of the Big Machine, made necessary by the new proposals from Brookhaven. It was no longer a case of simply copying the design of a tried and tested instrument, as the original intent had been, but of coping with numerous unusual problems, the outcome of which was highly uncertain. In October, 1952, on the basis of reports dealing with the "exciting new possibilities" of an "alternating gradient synchrotron" (AGS) brought back by the emissaries to America, the CERN Council declared its readiness to drop the already approved "Project I" in favor of the bold "Project II." Dahl's new assignment, incidentally, was predicated on the condition that he and his group were to determine, within a year, whether the daring new construction ideas were technically feasible at all.

From the very beginning it was clear that a price would have to be paid for the various advantages of the new zigzag principle, a seemingly exorbitant price. It was not to be paid in currency but in another medium of exchange: a precision never before required of an instrument of that magnitude. In earlier accelerators, the particles had a certain amount of freedom in traveling around the relatively spacious tunnel. In the new type of machine the particles would have to maintain a perfectly circular path, exact to hundredths of an inch, inside the narrow vacuum chamber. Before reaching their final velocity they would have to race half a million times around a track over six hundred yards long. Therefore, the slightest deviation in a single turn would be magnified successively, and would result in a large error. As a matter of fact, the bunches of protons would not survive their lightning journey. Instead of arriving at their target, they would prematurely crash into the tunnel walls.

In 1952, however, the precision of magnets was a long way from that required by the new construction. And that was only one of the many seemingly insoluble problems Dahl and his group had to face.

It was the very difficulties to be anticipated in the construction of the Big Machine that aroused the enthusiasm of the experts. Werner Heisenberg soon demonstrated the new "alternating gradient principle" to his students in Göttingen, with a ball that was made to roll along a wooden track having bumps and depressions on both sides. He told me that it was the "new idea" that had made the European laboratory really popular among the younger generation of physicists. For now they had a genuine incentive to manufacture a true prototype. Also, the spur of setting a record presumably had its effect. Never before had an attempt been made to produce a precision instrument of such dimensions.

The first difficulty encountered in the realization of the project was: it was not at all certain that a perfect circle, having a diameter of more than two hundred yards, could be drawn. Preliminary inquiries made of surveyors revealed that a ground plan with so large a circumference, precise to hundredths of an inch, had hitherto never been required. There were not even any instruments to measure such a giant circle. First, a new type of theodolite had to be developed, and special measuring tapes made from invar wire, which is not affected by temperature fluctuations, in order to fix the points through which an exact circle, one third of a mile around, could be drawn.

Early in the preparation stage of the proton synchrotron, a feature characteristic of modern large-scale scientific technology became manifest: almost as important as the ultimate goal are the side and secondary effects that arise in the pursuance of a particularly lofty purpose. A project of that nature sends out a shock wave that has a direct impact on the branches of research and engineering immediately adjacent to it, and then goes on to influence an entire epoch. It is evident that the activities of a large scientific enterprise like CERN can lead to progress not only in nuclear research. The excessive demands, made by a laboratory of this kind on the scientific and technological development divisions of industrial concerns, stimulate a great many new discoveries and inventions (in a variety of fields, from metallurgy to surveying, data processing, and electronics) which otherwise would not have made their appearance until much later, or not at all, perhaps.

More important even than the abundant harvest of technological by-products is the new mentality that is created. The scientific and technological endeavors of our time bring forth—for better or for worse—not only new goods but new attitudes as well, that point the direction of, and ultimately have greater influence on, the future than have the material goods that are produced.

III

In the windy, late fall of 1953, two young Englishmen and an attractive young lady signed in at a small Geneva hotel. They shut themselves up in their rooms, and for several days were hardly to be seen. Soon, visitors began to appear at all hours of the day and night. They were usually young foreigners in a tremendous hurry, barely able to contain themselves until their arrival had been announced.

Employees of the hotel thought, at first, that their new guests were members of a jazz band. They had overheard the two men being called the "Harwell Twins," and noticed that their suitcases were marked "fragile" and looked as though they might contain musical instruments. But no music was ever heard coming from their rooms, only a mélange of voices and an occasional mechanical clicking. The clicking was made by a small computer which had been assembled there, and which was now kept on or near the bed. The entire attention of the young lady, an expertly trained programmer, was devoted to it.

The young people belonged to the PS group of CERN. After extensive preliminary study, they had come to Geneva from all parts of Europe for their most important meeting thus far. They had been promised the use of facilities in the brand-new Institut de Physique of the university, pending the completion of their own quarters. But fed up with the many well-intentioned rules imposed upon them by their hosts, they soon chose to work in the less immaculate, but also less regulated, atmosphere of hotel rooms and cafés, or "Casbah," as the barracks springing up one by one around the spectacular construction site of the PS were called.

If these enthusiastic young "machine physicists" and their giant toy, the proton synchrotron, were to pass their examinations, all their calculations had to be absolutely correct, and they had to be prepared to supply convincing answers to any critical questions that might be put to them by their examiners. Over one hundred and fifty leading specialists in the field of nuclear physics and particle accelerators were expected to attend the conference in Geneva, at which the final decisions on the building of the world's largest machine would be made.

In the preparation phase that was drawing to a close, again there had been close collaboration between the European physicists and their colleagues in the United States. The husband-and-wife team of John and M. Hildred Blewett, from Brookhaven, went so far as to join Dahl's group in Bergen for half a year. The two Americans gave of their knowledge and experience to such an extent that they were explicitly thanked, later, in a CERN report, for their "invaluable aid" in solving problems connected with the new accelerator.

This close cooperation was especially remarkable in view of the fact that CERN and Brookhaven were basically competitors, particularly since Brookhaven also had decided to build an accelerator based on the new principle. From that time on, a kind of open competition developed between the two largest nuclear research laboratories of the Western world, which served as a model for fair play. In the contest for scientific honors, each one of the two institutions wanted to be on top, but that did not preclude assisting the other along the way, through advice; each even took pride in communicating to its friendly rival its latest findings—in the justified expectation that the other would do likewise.

The "race" between the builders of the CPS (CERN proton synchrotron) and the AGS (alternating gradient synchrotron) was always exciting and full of surprises, for a temporary lead by one group was soon tied by the other, which then could, itself, take the lead. Secrecy, "espionage," and trickery were naturally ruled out.

The older physicists were reminded, by this atmosphere, of the happier years of their science. The younger ones, however, who had been trained during a time of secrecy and security regulations, had to accustom themselves to it. Then they were all the more enthused over the complete freedom of expression that was so new to them. "That was the strongest attraction that the lab had to offer, at first," recalled one of the group of fifteen who had gathered in Geneva "to sell the PS to the v.i.p.'s," as they flippantly put it. Although they could not be guaranteed secure positions at the time, they were also not required to fill out questionnaires or be subjected to interrogation, as they would have been in national laboratories, during embarrassing examinations of their political and personal reliability. There were no secrecy oaths, no police guarding the gate—this carried greater weight than almost anything.

When, a few years later, an overzealous administrator suddenly decided to make access to the Geneva laboratory subject to permission, in less than twenty-four hours he was sent a resolution from the entire CERN staff, protesting his intent to transform the laboratory into a controlled institution. The resolution had instant effect. CERN remained as open as it had been from its inception.

IV

Soon after the plans for the accelerator had come through the crucial examination by experts in October, 1953, the members of the PS group were struck by two blows in succession. First, Odd Dahl, tired of wandering, declared that he would continue, for a time, to carry out his duties as head of his group (now in Geneva) and that he would represent it in negotiations before the CERN Council, but as soon as a suitable successor could be found, he would prefer to return to his homeland and his institute there. Then, Goward, who was to be Dahl's successor, came back one day from a trip to Paris in terrible condition. He had been accidentally involved in a police action against political demonstrators in the Latin Quarter and had been hit on the head and rendered unconscious. He died, several weeks later, of a brain disorder, which, though perhaps not caused by his having been manhandled, might well have been aggravated by it.

The PS group, responsible for the most important task of the laboratory, the construction of the Big Machine, was without a director from the beginning of 1954, until John Adams was given the most demanding post that CERN had to offer. He was only thirty-four years old at the time. Later events proved it to have been a wise choice.

Like Dahl, Adams had no standard academic training. He had begun as a mechanic; his father, a clerk, did not have the means to provide him with further education. But even as an apprentice in the workshop of an electrical engineering firm, the young man was conspicuous for his quick grasp and his industriousness. He was just about to be promoted when the entire factory was reduced to ashes one night during the blitz. Still too young to be drafted, Adams was taken up by the Telecommunications Research Laboratory of the Royal Air Force. There he acquired not only technical knowledge but also experience that later proved to be of great value, experience in laboratory teamwork and in the techniques of operations research, which were developed and tested by English scientists during the war.

The group with which Adams was associated developed the first successful secret weapon of World War II, radar, and put it into operation. Each member of the team, no matter what his age, had the reputation of being a mechanical genius. Although Adams was then only twenty-three years old, he was entrusted with the task of installing the new electronic navigation instruments in the Royal Air Force planes. Whenever anything went wrong with a new piece of apparatus, "Doc" Adams was called in, though he actually had no academic title or engineering degree.

"At the beginning, there were always difficulties when I was up for a higher position," Adams said later. "They wanted me —so far so good. But soon they would stammer: 'Only . . . only, the embarrassing thing is that you have no diploma to show.' And I would answer, 'Very well. Then why don't you take someone who does?' Especially after the end of the war, when I was assigned to building a cyclotron, there was a terrible fuss. I must have done a reasonably good job or they would hardly have sent me to CERN later on."

V

The diplomaless career of John Adams was one of the many manifestations of a technocratic style that began to take hold in the decade after the great war, a style that gave precedence to new methods over old rules, to necessities arising from reality over legalities that often lagged all too far behind rapidly changing actuality.

From a strictly legal standpoint it would not have been possible to start on the construction of the new laboratory at Meyrin, for instance, without first having taken care of all the legal preliminaries. In fact, France's Robert Valeur (President of the Council since the signing of the founding document on July 1, 1953), on his own responsibility, gave Secretary-General Amaldi permission to proceed with the most urgent preparations for actual construction, without any further delay. Therefore, the "first shovelful" of earth was turned by a derrick on May 17,

1954, even though some parliamentary ratification documents authorizing it were still lacking.

In some countries, France in particular, the CERN project had encountered political difficulties similar to those experienced earlier in Geneva. Had one waited, in order to act with strict legality, the best season for excavating would have passed and the entire construction been delayed by a full year, as a consequence.

Sir Ben Lockspeiser, Chairman of the Finance Committee and representative of the United Kingdom (the country that, after its lengthy hesitation about joining CERN, was the first to ratify the permanent Convention), was naturally asked to give his consent to this "illegal" measure, and he had done so. He was a practical joker, and opened a special meeting dealing with the credit necessary for the "unlawful construction activities" with the words:

"Gentlemen, it would seem that our main concern at the moment is not so much the well-being of CERN as that of our friend Amaldi. How can we manage to prevent him from being incarcerated for overstepping the limits of his duties?" Those present laughed, or smiled at least, but with some degree of discomfort. For, although the unlawful act could be justified, could even be deemed "absolutely necessary" from a practical standpoint, a not altogether harmless schism had arisen between technical and political decision-making, as is often the case in this era of rapid changes. Technology demanded quick, concrete, but perhaps one-sided answers, in an urgent situation. Politics had to weigh many factors one against the other, risking, in the process, being tardy and allowing the occasion to slip by in the meantime.

In this particular case, the activists among the engineers and scientists of CERN were, luckily, only a stone's throw ahead of the hesitating governmental representatives of some of the member states. Their actions soon received the expected parliamentary sanction. One after the other, the Netherlands, Greece, Belgium, Sweden, France, West Germany, and Norway followed the example of the three forerunners, the United Kingdom, Switzerland, and Denmark, by voting for ratification of the Convention. On September 29, 1954, upon receipt of the required number of ratifications, the "interim period" of CERN came to an end. And on October 7th of the same year, with the convening of its first meeting, the permanent European Council for Nuclear Research began to function.

For the transition period of eight days between these two dates, a grotesque situation existed, giving rise to many jokes. On hairsplitting, formal juridical grounds Amaldi, during that week, was the sole legal "owner" of CERN. No action could have been taken against him had he taken it into his head to abscond with the by then considerable assets of CERN.

With the appointment of Felix Bloch of the United States (originally of Switzerland) as the first regular Director-General of CERN, this legal state of emergency was terminated. Bloch soon declared, however, that he wished to return to research. He was succeeded, therefore, after a relatively short time in office, by the head of the Synchro-Cyclotron Division, the Dutch professor of physics Cornelis J. Bakker. The latter was to direct CERN for almost five years, through its difficult construction period. Shortly after his appointment for a second five-year term as Director-General, he was killed in a plane crash.

The formal laying of the cornerstone of CERN, which the facts had rendered anachronistic, occurred during Felix Bloch's term, on June 10, 1955, on the meadows and farmland of Meyrin, already partly under construction. For the duration of several formal speeches the bulldozers, construction machines, and supply trains were still. Then, the "disturbance" over, construction could begin again.

VI

1953: Preliminary studies for the building of the proton synchrotron.

1954: Completion of the design.

1955: Experimental development of individual parts, apparatus, systems.

1956: Placing of orders for the manufacture of individual parts with firms of member states.

1957: Manufacture of parts in several countries.

1958: Concentration and testing of the various instruments at Meyrin.

1959: Assembling of apparatus. First trial runs of the Big Machine.

A fine, logical time table. John Adams had worked it out with the help of his friend Mervyn Hine, and proposed to stick to it, and even managed to, in fact. But often it seemed that completion of the Big Machine would be delayed months, years, perhaps would not occur at all.

The tall, athletic-looking Briton with features rather too regular in a face somewhat too calm never showed signs of sleepless nights. Nevertheless, problems associated with the construction affected him so deeply that he was often under greater nervous stress during the construction period than during the most dangerous reconnaissance flights of the war.

First, there was trouble with the terrain. The ground where the Big Machine was to be located proved an unexpected problem. The fourth question, on the questionnaire that Kowarski had sent out, had asked for information on the quality of the terrain. The reply had been: "The ground is good. No difficulties are anticipated in connection with building foundations or bases for machinery and heavy apparatus."

The statement would have been true for normal technical

installations, even unusually heavy ones. But for an instrument wherein distances of a ten-millionth of an inch mattered, something that was solid under ordinary circumstances was not solid here. The same ground that supported without difficulty enormous buildings like the Palace of the League of Nations turned out to be insufficiently stable. This was shown in the first detailed examination of the terrain. André E. Decae and J. Gervaise, directing the preliminary surveying, had lowered pendulums and microscopes into shafts many yards deep, in order to study the bottom layer. Analysis revealed that the projected site moved about one twenty-fifth of an inch per hundred yards per month. The usual slight disturbances of ordinary buildings, evidenced years later in cracks in the walls, were intolerable for this construction, which, despite its ample proportions, had to function with the precision of a chronometer.

After numerous additional test drillings, sandstone was finally struck, at a considerable depth below the sliding moraine, and it seemed to be less mobile than the layer above. But the special instruments built in the machine shop of the PS group, and lowered deep into the ground, still registered slight tremors. Were they caused by earthquakes? Inquiries directed at the seismographic stations at Neuchâtel and Freiburg elicited the information that the region around Geneva is afflicted by about twenty slight seismic shocks each year. It was clear, then, that earthquakes alone could not possibly account for all the tremors. The movements in the horizontal plane, registered by the instruments, seemed more like the very slow but unmistakable rocking of a boat gently borne by the waves of the outgoing tide. The movements had a pronounced effect on the "perfect circle" that the vacuum chamber of the Big Machine was to describe; they deformed it, at times, by tiny fractions of inches.

People immediately lost themselves in a multitude of assumptions regarding the origin of the phenomenon. Was it construction work on the site that caused it? Shifts caused by underground rivers? The movement of the water in Lake Geneva?

Only after months of patient observation did the surveyors settle on what might be the key to the problem. It became more and more clear that the rocking occurred rhythmically, at intervals of half a lunar month; that is, it corresponded exactly to the ebb and flow of the tides. But Geneva is located hundreds of miles from the nearest seacoast. Was it possible that the ground of Meyrin was being rocked by the waters of the Atlantic? It hardly seemed likely, at first. But suddenly there was an astonishing confirmation of this supposedly fantastic hypothesis. At certain times of the year, a much more pronounced movement was recorded by the instruments than at other times. And the more pronounced movement coincided exactly with the time of the equinox, when the Atlantic strikes the West European coast with especially high tides. Thus, it really was the pounding of the sea that was being registered, more than a day's journey by car inland.

In order to eliminate these disturbances that might interfere with the functioning of the proton synchrotron, the architects had to devise a special system for shock absorption. They decided to sink eighty reinforced concrete piles forty feet deep into the rock layer of the terrain, and to set on top of them an elastic base which would support a concrete ring with a diameter greater than two hundred yards. In that way, the fluctuations and vibrations would be absorbed before they could ever reach the Big Machine resting on its complex foundation.

There was another factor to be considered: temperature. It is well known that changes of only a few degrees cause most materials to expand or contract to some extent. We usually take no notice of this "breathing" of the material world around us. But because of the small tolerances of the PS it might prove quite a disturbing factor. Therefore, a special air-conditioning plant was proposed, to keep the foundation of the ring at constant temperature. In addition, an arterial system of thin water pipes, supplied by continuously operating pumps, was planned for the foundation, which was to bear a load of thousands of tons. With these measures, it was hoped that the slightest change in temperature would immediately be spread uniformly over the entire ring.

VII

A feature of modern large-scale projects, regardless of the field in which they are undertaken, is that the many individual tasks required are not carried out in succession, as was true earlier, but are planned side by side and are often performed simultaneously.

These actions, going on in various places, cannot be described adequately in the chronological format of a report. If the reader wishes to learn how such an enterprise takes shape, how the various decisions and actions overlap and influence one another, how the leading participants are forced to have their minds on three or four different items at the same time, and, moreover, to travel, in imagination at least, through several periods of time, then he should not turn one page after another in sequence, but should instead stand before one of those planning blueprints from which a bird's-eye view of all stages of development of the growing project can be taken in at a glance. That kind of a representation might give the reader an idea of the feelings of the leading staff members of the enterprise, who are pulled back and forth by different tasks, are constantly under stress, but, at high points in their work, experience a kind of euphoria.

Project Director Adams, his immediate staff, and the heads of the subdivisions got together at least once a week—usually on Monday—for meetings of the "Parameter Committee." At those meetings the entire plan, consisting of thousands of calculations and blueprints, was worked out; later, during the period of its execution, it was nicknamed "the bible." The bible laid down the specifications for the "ideal machine," the height and width of the narrow chamber, for example, which was to be evacuated to one billionth of an atmosphere. There, the bunches of protons, already pre-accelerated to energies of fifty million electron volts in a linear accelerator, would be accelerated, by high-frequency fields, to an increasingly higher velocity, and hence to an increasingly higher impact force.

The book catalogued the genesis of an entire artificial world. For, strictly speaking, the Big Machine is not just one piece of apparatus, cast in a single mold, but is a conglomeration of a great many instruments, smaller and larger, simpler and more complex, whose interplay was to occur at speeds too high to be perceived by human senses. If a single vacuum pump were to jam, if a single one of the many servomotors were to stall, if a single electronic sensor were to fail, if only one of the hundreds of mechanical creatures were to work imperfectly, the result would be the breakdown of the entire organization of highly bred technical creatures.

For that reason, each individual part was "overdesigned," that is, specified to exaggerated precision. An example of the meticulous care that was exercised is provided by the work done in connection with the "source" of the future beam of protons that were to circulate in the machine. From the outside it looked like an unpretentious ceramic pot. In it, hydrogen was to be heated to a plasma, ionized, and transformed into free protons and electrons. Its supply tube alone had to be changed at least ten times before this relatively small "organ" of the giant body that was the machine functioned satisfactorily.

But that was nothing in comparison to the efforts required to make the one hundred electromagnets, each one almost five yards long, meet specifications.

It was not enough to place the individual units in their designated positions with an exactness of hundredths of an inch; it was necessary that the electrically produced magnetic fields behave precisely in accordance with the calculated predictions. That could only be achieved, however, if the thin metal plates, which were pressed together to form individual magnetic blocks, were almost identical in composition and mold, an "ideal" requirement impossible to satisfy with the commercial steel available in Europe.

The first tests revealed deviations from the calculated values that were far too great. These were due to irregularities and impurities in the metal from which the plates were made, a consequence of slightly different manufacturing conditions in the different foundries. Once, in a discussion with François de Rose, Robert Valeur, and several other members of the Conseil, Adams suddenly vented his discouragement with: "I could give you a million reasons why this machine will never function properly." The manufacture of more than a quarter of a million half-inch steel plates, with almost identical properties, posed enough problems to cause the entire project to fail.

It was in just this type of situation, however, that the young project director's almost irrational optimism and confidence in the future asserted itself. At first, some of his skeptical co-workers belittled this confidence, often not well founded in fact, as naïveté, but they were soon to recognize that this idiosyncrasy of their director was the outstanding—more, the essential—characteristic of a pioneer. Adams did not allow himself to be intimidated by the magnet problem for long. He ruminated over which member of his staff might have solved a similar problem before, and hit upon an Australian said to have more patience than an angel. Colin Ramm, on an assignment from the Commonwealth Meteorological Bureau during the war, had to polish optical lenses to an accuracy of four millionths of an inch. He developed, at that time, the combination of fanatical exactness and calmness necessary to a successful experimenter. In order to manufacture precision objectives, periscopes and microscopes, Ramm had gone directly to the factories to supervise personally the production of the special sorts of glass he required, before accepting them for further processing. That was the way he would act in this case, too.

Immediately upon assignment to his new job, Ramm dispatched scouts to factories in a dozen European countries in search of the best steel for the magnets. He finally found a plant in Italy that was willing to produce the highly sought "ideal steel," regardless of the many difficulties associated with its production. He then delegated supervisors from CERN to this plant, to watch over each phase of production of the desired 255,000 steel plates, on the spot.

But that was not all. Professor Karl H. Reich, a member of CERN for many years, describes the steps that followed:

"First, the unprocessed sheets were carefully annealed. Then, magnetic tests were made on numerous samples, and those outside the allowed range of fluctuation were sorted out. In the next operation the plates were mixed statistically, so that each packet of plates contained sheets from every production lot. Finally, the 1,020 finished packets of plates were individually measured on a special test platform and . . . distributed among the magnet units in such a way that the average value of each unit . . . was the same."

The first tests performed on models showed that the procedure would prove successful. The magnet problem—its most difficult aspect, at least—seemed solved. Meanwhile, dozens of other problems had cropped up, however, causing renewed brain-racking, demanding new ideas and above all new courage.

In order not to lose the accelerated "packets" of elementary particles, at a certain critical point in the acceleration of the proton beam there had to be a "phase shift" in the high-frequency system, which would take place within a millionth of a second. Could it be accomplished? Even before that, would "injection" of the beam into the circular track of the PS from a linear preaccelerator also work? Would the computer, which was to regulate the gradual increase in energy—the seven million individual pulses, which make the protons circle faster and faster—always send out its signals at the proper instant? Would the back signals of the beam to the self-regulating instruments of "beam handling" work?

So many question marks, so many individual experiments to test every one of the thousand individual parts that make up the collective, the Big Machine. In nine different countries and in more than a dozen different cities (Paris, Cologne, Milan, Mannheim, Eindhoven, Oslo, Geneva, and Zagreb, for instance) the many European firms cooperating on the construction of the PS had to perform rigorous stress tests on small-scale models. For years there was experimenting, rejecting, constructing anew, testing, changing, and re-thinking. Coils burned out, bolts deformed, pistons jammed, oil pipes leaked. "Nearly perfect" or "works in ninety-nine percent of the cases" was not acceptable. CERN was a relentless customer; it demanded the utmost in reliability. Not a few firms that had entered into agreements for stated fees, which had seemed high to them at first, now came to the realization that their costs might turn out to be greater than their earnings. When they claimed later, in their advertising, that above all it was an honor to have been associated with the Big Machine, that was all too true: they had to pay for the honor with considerable sums from their own budgets. They found their profit in greater prestige and increased skill.

VIII

Many of the specifications that Adams and his team requested could not have been met by an ordinary technical plant geared to mass production. Therefore a machine shop was opened in Meyrin, to handle difficult and novel custom orders.

This atelier attracted mostly the kind of worker who wanted more than merely to earn his keep. These were the individualists, the hobbyists, the inventors. They enjoyed the "nearly impossible," and were encouraged by Géo Augsburger, their temperamental foreman, to go about their business in their own way. These mechanics soon found they had more in common with their new colleagues, the scientists and engineers, than with the turners and grinders with whom they used to work. Upon being asked about their new occupation, they would reply: *"Nous sommes des chercheurs nous aussi!"* (We are also researchers!)

It was the common striving for the unknown, the making of tools that had not existed before, the feeling of being together in a great adventure, that united these "poets of technology" with the physicists, surveyors, electrical engineers, and programmers working at CERN. They had started out together on an expedition to the realm of the smallest dimensions. Theoretically, science had long ago predicted this new territory. Now one would actually be able to reach it, with the aid of the newest instruments, conceived by one man, designed by another, and built by a third. The man in the street is hardly aware of the existence of this "super-Lilliput," where the subnuclear reality is measured in microns and nanoseconds, in microcuries and picofarads. There, billions of points combined are not as large as a single dot on our printed page; there, untold billions of time units do not last as long as it takes us to pronounce a single word.

John Adams knew how to arouse in his co-workers a strong feeling for the common experience, and how to keep it alive. His early familiarity gained in English machine shops enabled him to talk to mechanics in their own language; his intelligence and alertness also won him the respect of the engineers and scientists with whom he dealt. Not only could he keep together a team of almost two hundred people with different occupations, nationalities, and temperaments, but he could also infuse them with enthusiasm. Were there any tensions or frictions? "Of course," conceded Adams. "It was impossible not to have them. But what was much more important was that all of us felt the need—were even possessed by it—to fulfill the task. We wanted to show the world that it was possible to have great achievements that are aimed not at destruction but at progress. Basically, I was not the one who gave the orders. It was the project itself that guided us and held us together. It helped a little, perhaps, that many of us were strangers in rich, sated Geneva. That brought us closer together. It was that we knew what we were living and working for. Not many people can say that of themselves these days."

An ideal leader of a team, which Adams undoubtedly was, does not necessarily have to be the most outstanding in a particular field. The specialty of that kind of person is not to be a specialist himself, but to have the broadest perspective possible. He must be able to handle co-workers who know more than he does in certain areas. He must inspire and encourage everyone, and give to some the self-confidence that had been undermined since their earliest youth. Adams possessed this gift of inspiration to a high degree. Therefore many turned to him, not only for professional advice but for private counsel as well.

While Adams was the heart of the PS group, his closest co-worker, Dr. Mervyn G. Hine, a brilliant, sensitive, quick-thinking English physicist, was regarded as the brain of the project. The two Englishmen, incidentally, were born only forty-eight hours apart—a fact which earned them the nickname the "Harwell Twins" when they started to work together in the leading British research center. A less well-balanced person than Adams might not have been able to tolerate, at such close proximity, so superior and unrelenting a critic. But the "boss" found the acuity, the knowledge, and the quick reactions of his "twin" to be indispensable supplements.

IX

By the end of 1957 the laboratory site at Meyrin finally began to take on the neat, orderly appearance that had been projected years before—to some it seemed a decade—by the architects' models. The crude, bare scaffolding had been transformed into tall, bright, modern buildings and spacious workshops, the muddy ground of the construction site had disappeared under the asphalt of straight streets and the grass of new lawns. Even the artificial hills ("Mount Citron," for example, named after a German physicist), that served as shielding against the radiation expected to result from the experiments, looked as if they had always been there. Only "Adams Hall," the headquarters of the PS group, remained unchanged. Surrounded by all the fresh, new glamour, it looked shabby and neglected.

The last two years of construction were especially hard for the builders of the Big Machine. Finally, they were about to assemble the individual pieces of apparatus that were arriving from all parts of Europe, into the one large proton synchrotron. In the surrounding area, a great deal had been completed during the six years that they had been playing with their giant toy. The "small machine" (the synchro-cyclotron) had begun to operate in 1957, and soon attracted the attention of the whole scientific world the following year, at the "Atoms for Peace" conference in Geneva, through an important discovery. The large administration building, with its offices, cafeteria, sparkling pool, lecture halls, and conference rooms, had by that time been inaugurated and was already being used for international conferences.

At one of these conferences there was talk of future accelerators that would far outstrip the still unfinished PS, in size, energy, and techical refinement. In 1953, the designers of the proton synchrotron had superseded, in their plans, the still unfinished "bevatron" at Berkeley. They were now faced with a similar prospect; their accelerator "had become a grandfather before even being born."

By 1957, a division for designing more advanced accelerators was set up in Meyrin. There, several physicists who had made important contributions to the design of the PS, Arnold Schoch of Germany and Kjell Johnsen of Norway, for instance, were busy planning the "next generation" of atom smashers—at a time when it was not at all certain that the Big Machine would function according to plan. One question especially remained that calculations or tests performed on models could not answer: would it be possible to pass through the "transition phase" ? This critical phase occurred because of the relativistic effects predicted by Albert Einstein, namely, that as the energy of the particles increased, their mass would also increase. The increase in mass produced side effects in this new type of machine that might result in the loss of the protons, accelerated by then to energies of more than 4 BeV.

In September, 1959, another conference on high-energy accelerators was held in Meyrin. The conference dealt mainly with new types of machines, and was quite well attended. The proposals and designs of Professor Matthew Sands of California attracted particular attention; they called for a two-story machine of 300 BeV (ten times more than the energy of the CERN proton synchrotron) with a diameter of more than a mile. Unexpectedly, at the start of a session John Adams asked for permission to make an announcement that was not part of the regular program. He informed the audience that the night before, on September 16, the proton beam had been injected into the vacuum ring of the new Big Machine from the linear accelerator for the first time. It had described its first complete circle without losing particles on the way. The announcement naturally caused a great deal of excitement. It took quite a while for the conferees to turn back to the accelerators of tomorrow.

But that first success had only been a trial run. The beam of the PS had not yet been brought up to total energy and not been sent around the track the necessary million times. The crucial question of whether the proton beam would survive the critical transition phase could not be answered by this partial experiment. Several Soviet scientists had still harbored strong doubts about the final success of the new gigantic accelerator. Professor Vladimir Nikitin presented John Adams with a bottle of vodka labeled "Not to be opened until 10.1 billion electron volts." This value was chosen deliberately because ten billion volts was the highest energy attained by the "synchrophasotron" in Dubna (not far from Moscow), since 1957 the largest particle accelerator in operation. The PS was expected to break that record by a factor of two and a half.

A pictorial survey of the Big Machines, their installations at CERN, Brookhaven, Weston, Dubna, and Serpukhov, and some of the men who helped create them.

This is a new type of industrial complex, which may become typical for our times: a research factory producing knowledge rather than goods. The aerial view shows CERN (Conseil Européen de la Recherche Nucléaire), one of the largest laboratory complexes of the world, financed by thirteen European nations. (PHOTO CERN)

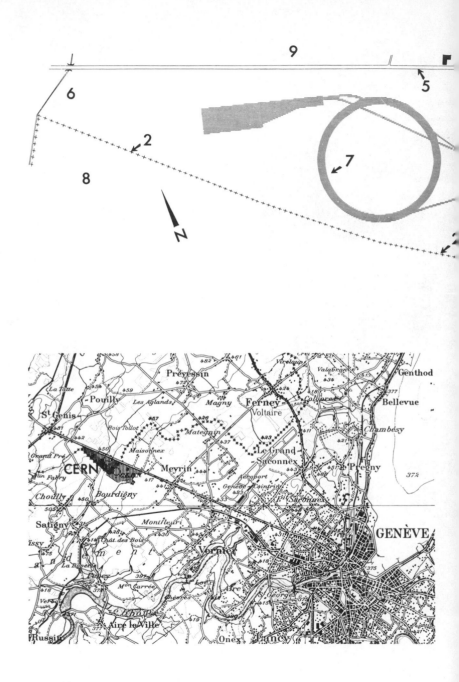

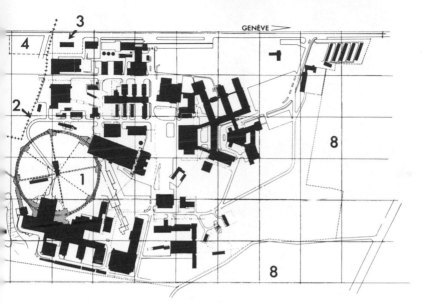

(1) 28 BeV proton synchrotron
(2) French-Swiss border
(3) Swiss customs
(4) New French customs
(5) Nationale 84 (Lyon-Geneva road)
(6) Nant de l'Ecra (stream)
(7) Intersecting storage rings
(8) Switzerland
(9) France

In reaching over the zigzagged line, the laboratory established itself in two sovereign nations: on the right of the frontier, the overcrowded terrain of Switzerland; on the left, the new intersecting storage rings on French territory. (PHOTO CERN)

The two main protagonists of the CERN story—the Englishman John Adams (left), the self-educated builder of the Big Machine; and the American physicist Victor F. Weisskopf (right), who turned this laboratory into one of the most important scientific enterprises of the world. (PHOTO CERN)

Bernard Gregory (France) succeeded Weisskopf in 1966 as director of CERN. (PHOTO CERN)

Discussions between physicists coming from all over the world to Geneva are sharp and intense. Blackboards are to be found in most offices. Weisskopf makes a point; Nobel prize winner Patrick Blackett seems doubtful. In such conversations, new insight grows and new theories are born. (PHOTO CERN)

In the control room of the CERN proton synchrotron, as in most parts of the lab, work never stops. Except during short closedowns for repairs, the Big Machine works day and night. (PHOTO CERN)

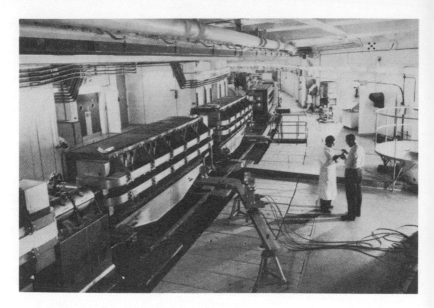

The 28 BeV proton synchrotron ring at CERN is 219 yards in diameter. In it, protons are accelerated up to almost the speed of light. A number of the 100 magnet units of 3400 tons each can be seen on their shockproof concrete supporting girder which is architecturally independent of the ring building. (PHOTO CERN)

The "beam" of billions of accelerated highly energetic nuclear particles transported by long "beam lines" is fed to several research teams and their apparatus in the East Experimental Hall. (PHOTO CERN)

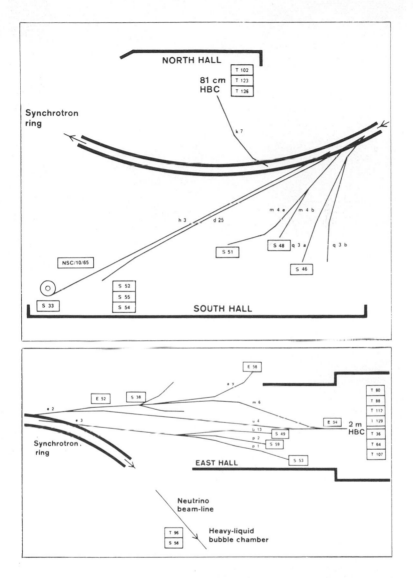

Not only one experiment at a time but a considerable number are run simultaneously on the Big Machine and the apparatus surrounding it. Here is a simplified layout of beams (small letters and single numbers) and the location of experiments (identified by their code numbers in boxes) performed on the same day in the three experimental halls of CERN. (PHOTO CERN)

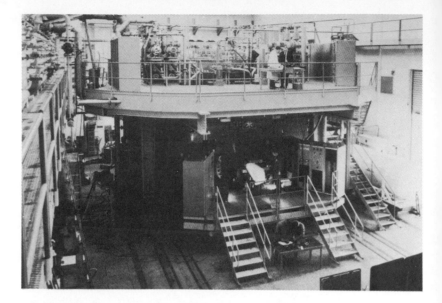

Bubble chambers (which have become Big Machines in their own right) make the subnuclear world visible. (PHOTO CERN)

As glimpsed in a bubble chamber: the universe inside the atomic nucleus — a world as deep and as rich in unexplored phenomena as that of space. Wherever tracks emerge from a point, some high-energy collision or disintegration is taking place. (PHOTO CERN)

Here an experiment is under way. The physicists check the automatic particle detection devices whose electronic complexity is plainly visible. (PHOTO CERN)

This aerial view of the 33 BeV alternating gradient synchrotron shows America's Big Machine at Brookhaven National Laboratory, Upton, New York. Some of the most important nuclear discoveries have been made at this laboratory since work began in 1961. (BROOKHAVEN NATIONAL LABORATORY)

The "next generation" of nuclear accelerators will be even bigger and stronger. This sketch gives a glimpse of the support facilities for the new U.S. 200 BeV Big Machine which is being built in Weston, Illinois. It may eventually reach energies of 400 or even 500 BeV—almost twenty times as great as the CERN and Brookhaven machines. (NATIONAL ACCELERATOR LABORATORY)

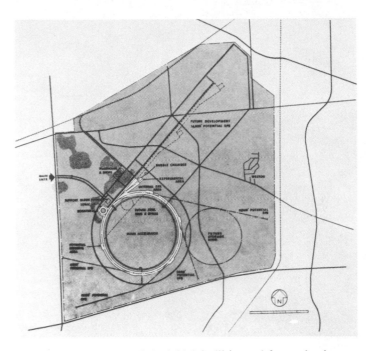

This is the master plan of the initial facilities and future development alternatives at Weston. The giant accelerator will have a radius of five eighths of a mile. (NATIONAL ACCELERATOR LABORATORY)

Robert Rathbun Wilson is Director of the National Accelerator Laboratory at Weston. (WIDE WORLD PHOTOS)

At almost the same time, Edwin M. McMillan (top), in the United States, and Vladimir Veksler (bottom), in the Soviet Union, developed the new principle of the synchro-cyclotron, making possible the acceleration of atomic particles to extremely high energies. (AMERICAN INSTITUTE OF PHYSICS; SOVIET LIFE)

It looks like a concert hall, but it is the home of the 10 BeV proton synchrotron in Dubna (USSR), which began to work in 1956 and was for a period of over three years the most powerful accelerator in the world. (TASS FROM SOVFOTO)

The magnets of the Dubna machine weigh 36,000 tons and the diameter of the ring is about 65 yards. The machine never worked in a satisfactory manner. (TASS FROM SOVFOTO)

One of the modern research laboratories in Dubna is seen from the old village adjacent to the grounds. (K. M. VAHLBRUCH)

With the modern 70 BeV proton accelerator, which started to function in Serpukhov (USSR) a few weeks before the fiftieth anniversary of the Russian Revolution, the Russians have again taken temporary leadership in the field of instruments for nuclear research. This outside view of the accelerator shows the large experimental hall and support buildings. (LUKE C. L. YUAN)

X

Finally, the last and most exciting stage began. After hundreds of examinations, major and minor breakdowns, conferences, repairs, hurried meetings, and repeated trial runs, all the preliminary tests of the individual parts had been completed. On July 27, 1959, the hundred units were magnetized for the first time; on September 16, the beam-handling system was put into operation; and on October 13, the high-frequency system was tested. Acceleration of the proton beam was first carried out successfully, though only for several thousandths of a second, on October 15. On October 22, an energy of 400 million electron volts (MeV) was attained, and on October 27 it was up to 1.5 BeV.

Then, nothing worked right any more. On Friday the thirteenth, in November, the radial control of the beam suddenly broke down. Something seemed to be wrong with the magnetic fields as well. None of the minor operations the machine doctors recommended did any good. The giant body of the patient, with its twisted, nearly 3,000-mile-long arterial system of pipes and cables, had to be probed and examined carefully, in order to locate the afflicted area.

Finally the source of the malady seemed to have been discovered. At one point along the vacuum ring the Geiger counters clicked wildly when brought close, indicating a high level of radiation. The diagnosis: the proton beam must have met an obstacle at that point in its path and made it radioactive. How could a blunder like that get through all the controls and countercontrols? A quick examination revealed that in the course of assembling the machine, two charts had been interchanged. Despite all the checks, nobody had noticed that a metal support protruded too far into the path of the beam!

Hardly had this disorder been cured when an extremely complicated high-frequency system, geared to high-speed switching within ten thousandths of a second, acted up. The method of cybernetic beam control developed in Heidelberg, in which the acceleration of the proton beam is regulated by its own feedback signals, would not listen to reason, and its master, Professor Carl Schmelzer, ordinarily easygoing, for the first time exhibited a nervousness that not even his beloved beer could combat.

Among those who, for days, had hoped in vain to witness the first full operation of the Big Machine, was Mrs. Blewett of Brookhaven, who had contributed tirelessly to the designing of the PS. She had postponed her departure several times—an additional postponement was impossible. On the morning of November 25th she would definitely have to fly back to the United States.

The day before, therefore, everyone tried especially hard to get the PS to top energy. The morning passed, the afternoon, and then it was evening. The men sitting before their instrument panels in the two control rooms, one located in the middle of the wide south ring of the machine and other off to the side, decided to give it a final try.

Shortly before 7 P.M., Dr. Hine, directing the experiment, gave the order for a new start. The hoarse alarm sounded, warning everyone to get behind the concrete shielding. Red lights flashed; magnets began to hum. Then, from over the loudspeakers came the words: "Stop! A door is still open."

Once more. It was almost 7:20. Again the alarm sounded, again the generators buzzed, again eyes were fixed on the glass screens of the oscilloscopes, where the beam would soon appear.

Again: "Stop!"

The disappointment was great. Once again it would not work. Tensions relaxed. Some of the control room staff said good night and went home. At 7:30 a last try, which no one took seriously at this point.

Adams spoke once again over the intercom to his helmsman Hine.

"Ready?"

"Ready!"

This time—they could hardly follow it as quickly as it happened—the greenish-white image of the beam formed bright and clear on the oscilloscope screen. In seconds the beam was up to 4 BeV. Now came the long-awaited and long-dreaded critical region of the "transition energy," and before one could fully grasp it, the beam had passed through, after having raced around the more than a third of a mile long track thousands and thousands of times.

Now the beam was up to 6 BeV, the highest energy the machine had yielded during the trial runs. In the control room they asked, through gestures: "Higher?" "Yes!" The program for the magnets was introduced, exciting them to a field strength of 12,500 gauss. Ten . . . 10.1 . . . 10.2 BeV—the Soviet record was broken; from now on it was the region of the unknown. Fifteen BeV . . . 18 BeV . . . 20 BeV . . . everything ran like clockwork. Not until 24 BeV, somewhat below the maximum possible 28 BeV, was the experiment interrupted. It was 7:35 P.M. They all fell into each other's arms. Beaming all over, Hildred Blewett could hardly utter a word for emotion.

The sober progress report issued soon after gave some further precisions: not only had the beam been accelerated to a record high of 24 BeV, but at the same time, in the very first attempt, ninety percent of the protons had arrived at the target. That great an intensity had really not been expected. Would the shielding be sufficient under these circumstances? was what immediately flashed through Adams's mind. He recalled the Saclay incident, where, only after a new accelerator, the Saturne, was in operation was it noticed that the radioactivity produced by the beam could constitute a danger for the operating staff.

But those were tomorrow's worries. First they celebrated their success with Director Bakker, who had hurried to the scene.

Nikitin's vodka, on hand for the occasion, was passed around, and a photograph of the oscilloscope screen stuffed into the empty bottle. It was sent airmail special delivery to Moscow, to notify its donor of the outcome of the bet.

The next day congratulations poured into Meyrin from all over the world. Adams and his staff only half-listened to the multilingual praises. They asked themselves which corrections on their PS should be made first; they thought of which scientific experiments they could now perform with their machine; they dreamed of the next, still larger projects they would realize some-day.

FOUR

The
Search

I

Completion of the 28 BeV accelerator was awaited with particular impatience by nuclear physicists the world over. They hoped to be able to explain, with the aid of CERN's PS and Brookhaven's AGS that were to begin operating a few months later, the many confusing phenomena that had made their appearance during the construction period of the two Big Machines and were not yet sufficiently understood.

A wisecrack in circulation had it that, in the period from 1953 (the year the 3 BeV cosmotron started up) to the end of the decade, "nuclear" physics had been completely transformed into "unclear" physics. The number of particles discovered, alone, exceeded all anticipation. And their behavior was so unexpected that one sort was christened "strange particles," while, at conferences, there was talk of nuclear "ghosts." The earlier idea that matter was composed of only a few "fundamental building blocks" could hardly be sustained under the altered circumstances. But for the time being, there was no convincing classification scheme for the constantly growing number of particles that were no longer so "elementary."

Of the four known fundamental interactions in the universe, gravitational interactions, electromagnetic interactions, "strong interactions" (those holding the atomic nucleus together), the fourth—the so-called "weak interactions" that are associated with the decay processes of radioactive elements (that are unusually slow, by subnuclear standards)—had recently commanded special attention. In 1956, Tsung-Dao Lee and Chen Ning Yang, two Chinese physicists residing in the United States, had shown that one of the basic unshakable laws of physics no longer held in "weak interactions." (Lee and Yang had, in May, 1956, advanced the daring hypothesis that "parity," or mirror symmetry, was not conserved in radioactive decay and in the decay of pions and muons. It was confirmed experimentally several times in January, 1957.) This might indicate that completely new, more profound but as yet not understood laws governed the innermost sanctum of matter.

One of the particles that might yield a clue to the unusual structures, which were counter to all previous experience, was the "neutrino." Bruno Pontecorvo, the Italian physicist who left for the Soviet Union under circumstances that are still obscure, once described the neutrino, in a popular presentation, in the following manner:

"Undoubtedly, the neutrino is the most astonishing of all the elementary particles. Its characteristic property is its unusual ability to penetrate, without difficulty, any obstacle in its path. That reminds me of the story of the man who went to the zoo and saw a giraffe for the first time. He murmured, 'That's impossible.' The reader may judge for himself: neutrinos can, unhindered, pass through iron a million times thicker than the distance between the earth and the sun. Even the most imperturbable might be skeptical, and ask, 'How can this impalpable particle be captured, then? How can one be certain it even exists?' "

As is the case with many discoveries in the natural sciences, the neutrino hypothesis owed its existence to a crisis: the contradiction between the theory held at the time and certain experimental findings.

In the investigation of one of the most common nuclear occurrences, beta-decay (transformation of a neutron into a proton with the emission of an electron, for example), it seemed that a certain amount of energy was "lost" in some unaccountable way. This contradicted one of the most fundamental laws of physics, conservation of energy. Should one allow an exception to the rule in this particular instance?

That embarrassing solution was indeed proposed by some of the most eminent minds in nuclear physics. Wolfgang Pauli, never content with oversimple explanations, sought for the source of the observed discrepancy elsewhere, however. After he had convinced himself that the new experimental data were correct, and not based on some erroneous interpretation, he concluded that a new particle, not yet observed, was emitted in the beta-decay process, and was responsible for carrying off the missing energy. Why had one never observed these "embezzlers of part of the energy capital" if they were present in such enormous numbers? Probably, argued Pauli, because they were entirely, or almost entirely, "invisible," that is, they had no mass, or what amounted to none, and possessed no electric charge. Only the third fundamental property of elementary particles, spin, did Pauli allot these suspected particles. If neutrinos really had no mass, then, according to the theory of relativity, they could never be in a state of rest, but would have to fly eternally through the universe, at the speed of light.

As implausible as the idea of a "rotating nothing" (a term

coined by Otto R. Frisch), put forth in 1930, may seem to the layman, it was nevertheless accepted by the physicists—at least until something better was forthcoming—because of the brilliant arguments advanced by Pauli. Nuclear physics had frequently gained ground through just such bold flights of imagination that are, only much later, shown to be more or less true, experimentally.

Soon after Pauli's neutrino hypothesis was published, Enrico Fermi propounded a mathematical theory of beta-decay based on that hypothesis, a theory that was verified later by experiment. It was also Fermi who coined the term "neutrino" (little neutral one) in the mid-thirties, for the new, still undetected particle.

Although one assumes today that neutrinos are very likely ejected by the billions, each second, from the giant nuclear hearths inside the stars, in a kind of cosmic vapor, and reach our earth (where they pass through everything, living or not), it was not possible to observe them in ordinary cosmic radiation because they hardly ever collide with other nuclear particles (that is, interact with them) but pass through them without leaving a trace. In 1965 the American physicist Frederick Reines and the Indian physicist Krishna Menon tried to "capture" some neutrinos by burying huge detectors in deep gold mines. There are indications that they found a few "genuine cosmic neutrinos."

Reines, together with Clyde L. Cowan, had, earlier, in the mid-fifties, furnished the first real experimental proof of the existence of these particles. At that time, he had brought his detectors very close to a natural source of neutrinos: the large reactors at the Savannah River Plant, which are used in the production of hydrogen bombs. No particle could penetrate the thick lead shielding other than neutrinos, which got through in quantities of 100 quintillion per second. Despite this enormous number, Reines and Cowan could record in their detector (a huge basin of water containing cadmium) only three neutrino events per hour, on the average. That was enough, however, to prove conclusively that neutrinos did not exist only in the imagination of some physicists. They really were there! To celebrate their feat, the two discoverers, working at Los Alamos at the time, threw a party. Each guest discovered under his napkin an elaborately wrapped gift. When he unwrapped it, he found nothing in his hand but an empty cardboard box. That is, it appeared to the eye to be empty. On the cover was written, and rightly: "Guaranteed to contain several hundred neutrinos."

But experimental proof simply of the existence of the long-sought particle was not enough for the physicists. Now they wished to learn more about its properties, for they suspected that a detailed investigation of the "little neutral one" might bring surprises, as had the discovery of the meson,* which also had been predicted only theoretically, at first.

Was there not perhaps—as had turned out to be true of mesons after several misconceptions—more than one kind of neutrino? The Japanese theoretician Shoichi Sakata had claimed that to be the case as early as 1943, and afterwards the thesis had been developed further by a host of other theoreticians (the Americans Emil Konopinski, Mahoud, and Julian Schwinger; The Bulgarian Markow; and the Japanese Nishijima).

Bruno Pontecorvo (and almost simultaneously, but independently, Melvin Schwartz of the United States) suggested, in 1959, at a conference in Kiev, that one should try to produce highly energetic neutrinos in the new accelerators that were soon to be completed, because these "little neutral ones" would interact more strongly than the less energetic decay neutrinos observed by Reines and Cowan. (At an energy between 1 and 2 BeV, an energy that can be attained by neutrino beams from the CERN proton synchrotron, it is estimated that a neutrino interacts ten thousand times more frequently with other parti-

---

* The quantum of nuclear forces predicted by Hideki Yukawa in 1935, the exchange of which, among the constituents of the nucleus, explains the strong nuclear forces.

cles—and only then can be observed—than do the neutrinos in reactor experiments, such as those of Reines and Cowan. There is an additional advantage: the neutrinos emerging from the accelerator are concentrated in a small cone, while those from a reactor are spread out in all directions.)

Pontecorvo had spoken about the matter, before he gave his sensational talk in Kiev, to his fellow countryman and former colleague, Giuseppe Cocconi. Cocconi was one of the last to see Pontecorvo before the latter's sudden disappearance in 1950. "We finally met again in 1959, in Moscow, at an astronomy conference," Cocconi recalled when I visited him in his small office at CERN. "Bruno drove me around in his car, during a break in the conference, because he wanted to show me the Soviet capital. His entire interest centered on the neutrino and the part it might possibly play in the energy budget of the stars. He and his friend Smorodinsky had just been working on the possibility that the neutrino might play a key role in the birth and death of the cosmos. The discussion became so intense that we completely forgot about the actual purpose of the excursion. So, of Moscow, I saw virtually nothing."

Cocconi was still spellbound by the excitement of the discussions when he met Hans Albrecht Bethe of the United States (formerly of Germany) who occupied the office adjacent to his at Cornell, and is one of the leading theoreticians of modern physics. Bethe also agreed that the study of highly energetic neutrinos might disclose an important new area of research, which should be left primarily to the Big Machines at Meyrin and Brookhaven, which were soon to be completed.

II

How this fruitful idea finally made its way to Meyrin, and CERN, and what reactions it produced, was related to me by Professor Helmut Faissner, in a long tape-recorded interview. (Except for deletions, Professor Faissner's statements remain essentially unaltered in style and in content, because a spontaneous report of this kind reflects the reality of research more precisely, perhaps, than do the intentionally colorless publications in the technical journals, which omit all the errors and confusions of everyday science. It is, however, a highly subjective account of a story colored by deeply personal relations.

"Cocconi came to the institute in great excitement one morning and said he hadn't slept a wink: there was a tremendously important experiment to be done at CERN, with the proton synchrotron—which wasn't even running at the time—a neutrino experiment. Our first reaction was: Cocconi is mad! Why, of all things, with a machine that produces all possible particles, protons, pions, k-mesons, antiprotons . . . why try to make neutrinos? Cocconi spent two nights calculating what the experiment would actually involve. One would have to have especially thick iron and concrete shielding to stop the trillions of different particles put out by the proton synchroton, until the only particles remaining were those that can penetrate all matter— almost without interacting—namely, neutrinos.

"It was clear, then, what an experiment like that would involve. What was not clear was how one could furnish convincing experimental proof of these extremely weak interactions.

"The problem of shielding was rather difficult, for it was shielding of one part in a trillion or more. It was also not clear with what probability the process would actually occur. But we heard from Bethe that Lee and Yang had dealt in detail with the theoretical aspects, and had calculated just how high the probability would be. The idea itself was originally expressed by Schwartz in the United States—and, shortly before, independently, by Pontecorvo in Russia. Cocconi wrote to Lee, whom he knew from a visit to the States, and Lee replied that most probably the experiment was impossible with the intensities expected from CERN's proton synchrotron. Higher intensities were necessary. . . .

"Several letters went back and forth. Reines wrote from the

United States—Reines, who had been the first to demonstrate the existence of the neutrino. He thought that in view of the low intensities a giant counter made from several tons of water should be used. Then some people at CERN began to show interest. Cocconi, Bernardini, and several others turned over in their minds whether a giant counter would really be the right thing. For the real question was: does one gain anything by proving that neutrinos exist? After some deliberation one had to admit: one doesn't gain a thing. That the neutrino exists, is known.

"What should really be asked was specific questions. First: is the neutrino produced in the decay of a pi-meson from an accelerator really identical to the neutrino emitted in beta-decay? The other question was: what does the distribution of the weak interaction charge of a nucleon look like? In other words, can one use neutrinos to 'illuminate' nuclear particles, in the same way that Robert Hofstadter had used beams of electrons?

"Then the theoreticians got all worked up, for it was clear to them instantly that neutrinos might provide the possibility of seeing a certain kind of structure in the nucleon that could not be seen before with any other means; it could not be seen with electrons, for instance.

"When I heard the formulation of the problem, I was convinced that this fundamental problem *had* to be solved. It was clear that there were very few places in the world—actually, only CERN and Brookhaven, with their sister machines—where the experiment could be performed. I thought very hard about it for several days. I was convinced that someone had to do it, and it seemed natural to me that Cocconi should do it. If not Cocconi, then some other well-established physicist who had a group at CERN.

"But a strange thing happened. First Cocconi, and then others—actually everyone in a position of importance at the time —said they did not feel like doing the experiment. The techniques were unfamiliar. Up to then, people had worked with bubble chambers of only, at most, a few pounds, or with some

100

small counters with surfaces of, say, several square inches. That was all they could handle. They could produce beams, could scatter them, could see with what probability a certain beam of particles is absorbed in a layer of material, with what probability it passes through. Those were all well-defined, quick experiments, requiring known techniques.

"Since we knew so little about what happened at high energies, it seemed to most people that it didn't make much sense to start working with counters with areas of square yards, or detectors weighing ten or a hundred tons, or, as Bernardini proposed, with spark chambers that were really not fully developed.* For years, spark chambers had not worked properly. Physicists claimed they were similar to the Geiger counter, an instrument that had been superseded. . . . There was general resistance, therefore. After a while Cocconi lost interest, the others as well, and at every one of the many discussions that were held on planning the experimental program for the proton synchrotron, the question would come up somewhere toward the end: shouldn't we do a neutrino experiment? But no one wanted to tackle it."

III

The early deliberations described here by Faissner occurred toward the end of 1959, in the months when the Big Machine neared completion and finally in the last week of November underwent its first test with surprising instant success.

Actually, the general expectation had been that the unbelievably complicated instrument would first have to succumb to the entire series of infantile ailments. But that did not happen, because John Adams, Mervyn Hine, and their assistants had managed, through their insistence on the greatest possible pre-

---

* In the spark chamber the passage of a particle is marked by a spark discharge that occurs in the space filled with a noble gas between metal plates held at high voltage.

cision, to have the sources of error as few as possible, with the minutest possible deviations from the requirements of almost all of the thousands of parts of the PS.

"In fact, our machine was finished prematurely," recalled one of its builders. "No one had really anticipated that before the end of 1960 experiments could be performed with the PS, and therefore by the beginning of the year a detailed experimental program had still not been worked out."

John Adams speaks with special feeling about the "black year" that followed the completion: "It soon turned out that the number of auxiliary instruments for an experimental program was insufficient. . . . These errors in planning and delays were caused mainly by inexperience. Due to the absence of modern accelerators in Europe for so many years, no one could gain experience in dealing with such high energies. . . . Organizational procedures, which are absolutely essential for experiments on these machines, were abhorred by many European physicists, and so a lot of time was wasted on discussions of the significance and working methods of physics. All in all, they were rather depressing experiences, especially as they followed so soon after the wild jubilation over the immediate operation of the Big Machine."

There were many other reasons why 1960 was a year of crisis at CERN. Since the more than $55 million that were ultimately spent for constructing the PS turned out to be double the estimated amount, the governing Council of CERN demanded strict economy during the next three years. Therefore, many purchases that were necessary could not be made. Also, cooperation with European universities was not yet entirely smooth. There were complaints that visitors from other institutions were being discriminated against, in favor of permanent members of CERN. On the other hand, foreign teams, working with such an unusually large apparatus for the first time, appeared somewhat helpless and dissatisfied. To cap it all, the "builders" of the machine, only yesterday in the top roles at CERN, were now forced to cede their leading positions to the theoreticians and experimentalists who, because of the nature of their work, were not able to outline for the laboratory community such clear and well-defined goals as the construction of a huge technical piece.

A series of internal crises resulted. The low point came when the popular Director-General, Bakker, was killed in a plane crash during a visit to the United States. The laboratory, plunged into mourning, remained for weeks without a head, until John Adams was finally appointed to the position. He was actually supposed to return home, in order to take over the directorship of the new national institution for research in nuclear fusion, in Culham. Nevertheless, he filled the opening at CERN. For various reasons it was not an ideal solution; first, because Adams could only devote half his energies to CERN because of his commitments in England, and, second, because he was soon involved in conflicts with several scientists who felt they had to defend their rights of inspiration and spontaneity against the pressure of "machine physicist" Adams for organization and efficiency.

Here, we once again witness the deep conflict within modern research which was touched upon earlier, and which will make its appearance again and again in these pages: the difficult transition between a time when scientific efforts are made with modest means but great freedom, in small or medium-sized academic institutions, and an epoch of "research factories," with their enhanced technical possibilities and consequent marked personal (perhaps even spiritual) restrictions.

A particularly good judge and witness of the entire development, who was, in addition, at CERN during the critical year, expressed his opinion as follows: One would not be very wrong if one were to regard that conflict as a contest between the new style of research inherent in Big Science—which was then familiar only to some French and British members of the laboratory, through their wartime experiences—and the traditional university style as practiced by the Italians, and the Germans, Dutch, and Scandinavians as well.

103

He pointed out to me, in detail, that most of CERN's physicists came from universities, and were proud of the intellectual tradition that for centuries had been the basis for the greatness of European science. They were not yet sufficiently aware of the obligations that the giant material devices of contemporary physics imposed upon them. As Adams was not an academician, they did not want to accept the necessary compromises from someone like *him*. This was, incidentally, a stage of development that their American colleagues had gone through some years earlier. Later it became the task of Weisskopf,* with his deep understanding of European traditions and his familiarity with American conditions, to guide CERN through this difficult transition period.

But we are still in the tense atmosphere of the year 1960, when it was not easy to push plans for a neutrino experiment through. Dr. Faissner gives the following account:

"Things went on this way for months and months. Bernardini and Cocconi took part in the project for only half or one quarter of their time. Bernardini thought more and more about the concrete experimental details, but he was extremely hesitant. Reines's large counter was certainly not the most appropriate thing, and there were other proposals from the Rome group. Amaldi and several others suggested that water pipes, over thirty feet long, might be buried somewhere; then, by observing the light flashes produced by a particle inside the water pipes, one could determine whether it was an electron or a muon. The advantages and disadvantages were discussed. The Rome group was about to try out a small pipe. But everything was quite vague and uncertain. Leon Lederman and Schwartz of Brookhaven spoke of imbedding several thousand Geiger counters in lead, and then trying to determine whether the neutrino produces only a muon, or, perhaps, an electron. Things went back and forth, and there was no real progress.

* Adams's successor, starting in 1961.

"It seemed quite natural to me, at the time, that Cocconi's group, to which I belonged, should do the experiment. But after some weeks of hesitation, it was decided that it would not be done. People were simply too conservative to devote serious thought to counters yards wide. After a while they said: 'We realize fully that this is good physics, but there is so much other good physics that can be done more quickly, with much less effort, with more precision and more elegance. If anyone is interested in doing experiments on neutrinos—by all means let him do them. In any case we will not.' But since something had to be done, a coordinator for the neutrino experiment was appointed—Bernard Hyams of England. . . .

"Apart from the people in the Nuclear Physics Division, the bubble chamber people around Ramm, the Australian, were also interested in the problem they were in the process of searching for—problems they had pushed through the construction of the large bubble chamber, and Jack Steinberger, on a visit from Brookhaven, had the right experiment for the chamber. So the two groups established some kind of contact.

"However, before becoming seriously involved in such a project, one had to know something about the radiation background.* The background presents quite a delicate problem: neutrons produced in the machine, or muons resulting from the decay of pions, can, under certain circumstances, simulate neutrino events. These disturbing factors can become so large that they make it impossible to do the experiment.

"In May, 1960, we were assigned a few shifts on the proton synchrotron to study the radiation background. Perhaps it was hoped that the background would be so large that the whole project would be abandoned straightaway. Hyams, some American visitors, and I quickly assembled some of Hyams's old counters and made them work. At the same time Hahn, from

---

* Undesirable particles that cannot be filtered out or absorbed and therefore mislead the observer.

Freiburg, brought a small bubble chamber, with a capacity of a few quarts, to the PS. Krienen (Holland)* and Roberto Salmeron (Brazil) worked on it, but Steinberger (U.S.) really knocked himself out over it. After several days and nights of measuring, it was clear that, though the problem might be difficult, it was solvable in principle.

"At the end of this very hectic period of initial preparations in the late spring of 1960, Bernardini concluded that the experiment was possible, and that it should be done with a very large detector, with one larger than the available bubble chamber, in any case, simply because the anticipated rate of events was so small. It was estimated, on the basis of not very good calculations and not very good arguments, that one could expect, per ton of material, at most *one* event per day. Steinberger had estimated ten per day. But one night, Bernardini and I concluded together that that was much too optimistic. And when Krienen and Salmeron redid their calculations, the one per day went down to three tenths per day. Even that turned out to be too high. . . .

"Not enough consideration had been given to the fact that the proton synchrotron, basically, was not well suited to neutrino experiments. The magnets were so close together that the pions were forced to emerge through the small space between two magnets. They still had to be deviated, focused, defocused in magnetic fields. All that was very difficult to control. . . . It seemed a bit risky to have a single counter of only half a ton, so that one might expect one event every second day, perhaps. Simple-minded people like me came to the conclusion that the counters should weigh ten tons. . . . The first detector I designed afterwards, in all innocence, without knowing much about the technology of large counters, was to weigh seven tons.

"Who was to decide which experiments were to be done?

* The nationalities were added by the author in order to emphasize the number of different countries taking part.

That was not well established at the time. It depended on spontaneous discussions. Hyams called a meeting. People interested in the neutrino experiment were invited. Naturally I went. His first question to me was a bit condescending: 'Did you do any detailed calculations?' I looked down at the floor, somewhat embarrassed, and said no, they weren't so very detailed, but I had certain general ideas about how things could work. He finally accepted that.

"When the first experiment on measuring the radiation background was performed, it showed that the experiment was actually not so hopeless. As a consequence, I made a detailed proposal and sent it to Hyams, and to Bernardini, of course. Bernardini said: 'It would seem that a new group has to be formed to construct this detector of at least ten tons. Since you were very much involved, why don't you head the group and build the detector?' Naturally I was extremely pleased. Then I went on vacation. When I came back from my vacation, however, I found that the opponents of the neutrino experiment had triumphed again: my group had been dissolved.

"Why? Perhaps it was because the general attitude of reasonable and conservative people was as simple as the following. First, the experiment is at the brink of not being possible. Second, if it can be done, it should not be by a completely unknown and unestablished young man, who obviously doesn't know anything about anything, who proposes absurd counter arrangements, who thinks nothing of building counters with surfaces yards wide, while any reasonable person knows how difficult it is to make a counter of, let us say, even twenty square inches, work properly. In any case, the conservative side had won, and after my vacation I had no choice other than to sit in my laboratory, apart from the main stream, and to think about how the experiment could be made palatable enough—cheap enough, in other words—and sufficiently undisturbing to other people that it might be accepted after all."

IV

While Dr. Faissner was still struggling with his problems, the attitude at CERN toward a neutrino experiment had undergone another change. According to his report:

"Luckily, one of the famous international high-energy conferences was held at that time, in Rochester, New York. There, people were groping around in a similar way . . . however, the attitude toward the experiment was quite positive, probably because of the influence of Schwartz and, above all, Lee and Yang. Besides, at just about that time, almost simultaneously in several places in the United States, the spark chamber was developed for use in experiments in high-energy physics. Actually, the spark chamber had been known for some time. In Germany, without attracting much notice, a man named Bagge had put one in operation somewhere outside Hamburg. In the United States, within a few months in fact, some successful experiments had been performed with it, with the effect that public opinion turned immediately toward the spark chamber. That, coupled with the generally favorable reception that the first groping ideas on the neutrino had met at the conference, suddenly made the mood at CERN go from 'minus infinity' to 'plus infinity.' It was decided that the neutrino experiment would be done. And it would be done with highest priority."

That was only one of the first significant experiments that were attempted with the proton synchrotron at CERN, and its preparations alone lasted for months. Faissner, whose group was still working on the previously planned liquid counter, gives the following account of this phase of the experiment.

"Most of the young people were very suspicious of us. They didn't believe that we would be able to fabricate, within only a few weeks, an apparatus so large and complicated. The 'neutrino operation' was in progress, and had been extremely well planned—but it was hectic and much too fast. We had to swear solemnly that we would be ready with our counters on January 15, first thing in the morning, for the march to the PS. The bubble chamber had already been put into official operation, to observe neutrinos. In order to install all the complicated pipes, cables, concrete blocks, supports for the shielding against cosmic radiation on the roof, and all that, a very tight time schedule was required. The proton synchrotron engineers showed us how to manage. It was almost like a military operation. Every eight days there was a committee meeting, at which everyone had to report on his progress and state whether he was keeping to the schedule.

"The bubble chamber and our counter setup often were in each other's way. Dozens of possibilities were discussed. Should the counters be in front of the bubble chamber, next to the bubble chamber, behind the bubble chamber? Finally it was decided that the counters would go in front of Ramm's bubble chamber. Then there was an additional decision: another bubble chamber—that of André Lagarigue of the Ecole Polytechnique, who also was to take part in the neutrino experiment—goes in front of the counters. It was a highly complicated problem in logistics, and it was of decided importance that everything should be completed on schedule. We succeeded, in fact, after several rough days and nights (and working all through Christmas). On January 15, 1961, at daybreak, we appeared at the designated spot.

"It was a Sunday. We had procured a dolly, and our counters were set on it, together with their giant iron supports that we had built in our machine shop in a few days—also in day and night shifts. When we got to the spot at the South Hall of the proton synchrotron, we were astonished: the opening that was supposed to have been broken through the wall did not exist. There was only one workman there, drilling a small hole in the wall with a pneumatic drill. That cost us half a day. We simply had to wait, because everything else was blocked. Finally there was a primitive passageway, and we could start to set up our counters."

V

What do scientists actually do when they sit before their control panels, appearing to be not looking at them, while numerous measuring devices labor for them by lighting up, drawing with mechanical pens, tracing light curves, clicking, rasping, hissing, or making hollow sounds at regular intervals? Faissner's description of the first phase of the neutrino experiment, still devoted to preparation and setting up of experimental apparatus, gives us some insight into it.

"We were the first to begin large-scale measurements of the 'background,' very systematically, step by step. At the beginning of February we had our first results. Naturally, everyone wanted to know them the very next day. We had to give reports every few days, and that made it easy to see that the systematic building up of shielding had enabled us to make the background relatively low within a short time. We supposed that the remaining background was due to cosmic radiation. We asked the proton synchrotron engineers whether they could reduce the duration of their 'beam pulses,' for, if the beam pulse were shortened, the cosmic ray background would be reduced correspondingly. At first we thought we might be able to observe neutrinos, even with this simple counter system. But that hope was unfounded —the disturbing background remained. It was only much later that we were able to explain that it was due to a weak spot in the shielding, and the muons were spitefully sneaking through.

"We still had no spark chamber at that time, and it soon became clear that if we wanted to go on, then we had to have something that recorded not only the fact that a particle had passed through the counter, but also *where* it had passed through. But the spark chamber was still looked upon at CERN as a somewhat complicated and unreliable instrument.

"In several weeks of hectic preparation we managed to make the area of our counter system ten times larger, to refine it, and to equip it with hundreds of light-sensitive electronic devices. To substitute for the spark chamber we lacked, we talked the cloud chamber group into hauling an old cloud chamber out of the attic, stuck five tons of lead into it, and had this slow, heavy monster controlled by our speedy counters. Everyone worked to the point of collapse. I suggested several times that we take it a little easier, but that was rejected completely. We had to observe neutrinos by this June at all costs. Otherwise, Brookhaven's machine might steal this important discovery right out from under our noses. A kind of neurosis seized us: a 'big discovery' complex.

"By the last meeting, all logistics problems had been settled to everyone's satisfaction, all schedules had been met, the bubble chamber (which had also been completed in day and night shifts) was operating, the shielding had been set up according to plan, all the supply tubes were functioning, a place for our electronics had even been found, the counters were in place, the cloud chamber was working. . . . We were all somewhat exhausted, but slightly exhilarated, since we had finally made it. Now there was actually nothing more to do than to switch on the beam and to wait for the first neutrinos to appear. At that moment, at the end of the meeting, Bernardini rose and said: 'Listen, gentlemen, have you thought enough?'

"Everyone was a little embarrassed. Bernardini is known for making inappropriate remarks on occasion. But to ask, at the end of minutely planned 'operation neutrino' whether one had really thought enough—after our weeks and months of thinking day and night how we could best do it—that was really too much! But as a matter of fact, several weeks later it turned out that we hadn't thought about it enough. Some minor side effects connected with the technical design of the proton synchrotron had simply been overlooked."

VI

The man who first made this crushing discovery was a Swedish physicist by the name of Guy von Dardel. Actually, he did not belong to any of the teams that were particularly involved in the experiment, but had been called in only temporarily, for consultation. As he came "from the outside," and was not a victim of the "neutrino neurosis" Faissner described, he could keep a cool head and figure out exactly whether the intensity of the beam of pi-mesons (pions) ejected from the machine (that decay in flight into muons and neutrinos) was high enough. Usually, the beam is relatively broad. But at CERN's PS the situation was somewhat different. In Faissner's words:

"Von Dardel found a flux of pions that did not at all agree with the calculations made earlier, and he also found that this flux behaved strangely. The very strong focusing effect (pinching the beam) was somewhat different from what had been expected. That made him suspicious. He didn't have to move tons of counters, so he could really think about the problem objectively, and within a few days he had convinced everyone of the correctness of his thoughts. Then, we all slapped our hands to our foreheads and said: 'How could we have overlooked something like that?'

"It was, naturally, a tremendous shock. In preliminary work, von Dardel estimated that the flux was indeed lower by a factor of eight. Some time later we corrected that, on the basis of more precise data. But still, a factor of five remained. However, it was clear that, with a reduction by a factor of five, the experiment as it had been planned originally, was meaningless." (Today, incidentally, some are of the opinion that it was only a factor of three—and one could have gone ahead without difficulty.)

"Naturally those few people—Max Reinharz, Maria Ferrero, and I—who had worked on the counters, did not want to throw in the towel, by any means. We had invested so much energy.

We saw the possibility of at least measuring the probability that a neutrino produces an event. That would in itself be something, but, as a statement in physics, it would really be a bit too crude. To make spark chambers within a short time also seemed unlikely. I had been repeating that we needed large counters. And we had those already. Therefore, why not quickly build some additional spark chambers, very simple ones made from a few metal plates stuck together with Plexiglas, something that we could do in a few months, after our experience with counters? But the confidence of the administration in the neutrino people had been shaken, and this project was rejected out of hand. There was nothing we could do. So, from the summer of 1961 to the end of the year, we tested the technical conditions under which the spark chamber operates and discussed what a refined detector, weighing many tons, should look like. After a good deal of hither and yon, and much reluctance on the part of the administration, it was finally decided, shortly before Christmas, that we could in fact build this large apparatus.

VII

"In the meantime, Brookhaven had built large spark chambers. They had started their project at about the same time we had ours, in the summer of 1961. While we were still struggling with the radiation background, and were trying, by hook or by crook, to observe neutrinos, they were devoting all their energies to the experimental setup, and faced their shielding problems later, in January, 1962. I was there at the time, for a few weeks.

"The conditions in Brookhaven were similar to ours, except that the magnet units of the proton synchrotron were separated more. The neutrino flux was somewhat greater, therefore, than at CERN. In addition, the Brookhaven people had iron shielding, because they had been able to have an old cruiser scrapped and had taken the steel plates. Switzerland could hardly be expected to supply us with a battleship.

"I left Brookhaven convinced that Schwartz, Lederman, Steinberger, and their co-workers would surely see neutrino events. I was not so certain whether it would be possible at this time to answer the question: one or two kinds of neutrinos? The experimental difficulties were enormous. The background of neutron effects was very large. It was a long, tedious struggle slowly, slowly, to reduce the background. When I was called back to CERN, Schwartz drove me to the airport at New York, and we talked about what the prospects were. He was still skeptical. As fate would have it, that very day his group saw their first event: an extremely long muon track—it was clear to everyone: it was a muon produced by a neutrino—and some secondary products. From that moment on, the experiment made steady progress.

"When we learned from letters, or telephone calls Cocconi received from friends in the States, or from CERN people working at Brookhaven and writing that great things were about to happen, it began to look as if the first answer might come out in this phase of the experiment. All that occurred very early in the spring of 1962. I phoned Schwartz. He told me that they had a whole series of candidates for neutrino reactions, and the muon tracks were extremely long. A few CERN people were there on a visit and saw the pictures themselves: it was clear—they were really neutrino events! . . .

"The lab at Brookhaven allotted more and more time to the neutrino experiment. The experimenters were given much more time on the machine than they had asked for originally, with the argument that if things didn't go well, they would need more time in order to set them straight; if things did go well, they would need the time all the more, to wait for events. Naturally, I was quite depressed at first, but I got over it early in the year, and wasn't so surprised when, in June, the big announcement came, that the second kind of neutrino had been found, and not from a publication in a physics journal—something like that is on the front page of *The New York Times* nowadays.

"We were busy testing our first large spark chambers in the

beam of the proton synchrotron at that time, and since we once again had something to do and were working day and night, it didn't hit us so hard. We were actually even happy, because we saw that the Columbia people had done the right thing—they had done it even better than we had expected. . . .

"While we were still somewhat hesitant about which direction we should now take, Yang gave us a tremendous amount of help. He said: 'It's true that the Brookhaven people made the discovery. But basically, we all knew it in advance.' It is also true that Lee and Yang had been fully convinced beforehand that the two neutrinos had to be different. They were equally convinced that weak interactions—that is, neutrino physics, if one prefers—had to take place through the exchange of a quantum in the same way that electromagnetic interactions take place through the exchange of a light quantum. (According to quantum field theory, to each field there corresponds a particle, or quantum.) Yang told us that it was obvious what we had to do. We had to try to find a different particle, the 'intermediate boson' (named after the Indian physicist Bose*). 'It must exist!'

"I was somewhat puzzled. There we were, surrounded by our spark chambers—Krienen, who had worked out all the techniques for the spark chambers, Yang, and I. I asked Yang: 'How can you be so certain this boson exists?' He replied: 'Well, I'm not one hundred percent certain. I'm not as certain as in the case of the two neutrinos. But if this particle doesn't exist, then we don't understand an essential point about nature. If all the symmetries discovered in the last few years are to have any true meaning, then they have to be traced back to this particle. Therefore, you should gear your entire experiment to finding this particle—if it's there.'

"He gave us two very important pieces of advice. First, that it was essential to continue, for there was still much more to be explained; and second, that we had to put aside any other

* Sir Jagadis Chandra Bose (1858-1937).

problems we could think of, in order to concentrate on finding the boson."

VIII

"Although Brookhaven had captured the second neutrino before we had, we wanted to do the experiment better, and to dig deeper into this newly uncovered field." Those words sum up the mood at CERN, after the recovery from the first shock. The new Director-General, Victor F. Weisskopf, who had been in a serious car accident soon after taking office, had been confined to his bed for months. Now on his feet again, he could finally direct his lab, with full authority toward a new goal.

The discovery at Brookhaven had been based on the analysis of only fifty spark chamber photographs of neutrino events. Among them were thirty-three indisputable observations in which the "second" neutrino had been positively identified. They formed the meager basis of a paper by Schwartz, Lederman, and their associates, that attracted a great deal of attention and was widely discussed in almost every nuclear physics laboratory in the world.

How could the average rate of neutrinos be increased—in Brookhaven it had been only one event per day—to a degree where comparisons between a number of different exposures could be made? That was the first question that was being posed in Meyrin. The second concerned the detector. If one wanted more detailed information about the neutrino and its interactions, one had to set up, in addition to spark chambers —which had been used in Brookhaven—at least one bubble chamber containing freon, a heavy gas, as a trap for neutrinos. But that made sense only if a hundred times as many of these elusive particles could be produced. Only by concentrating all the intellectual and technical resources of a large laboratory could a breakthrough be made. Three different fronts were being attacked at the same time. First, the shielding against the disturbing background had to be improved and strengthened. Second, attempts had to be made to make the neutrino beam very much more intense, for it alone was to pass through the shielding filter. And third, all detectors, spark chambers, counters, and bubble chambers had to be refined considerably.

On the strengthening of the shielding, Faissner reports: "By the beginning of 1962, it had become clear to us that we shouldn't deprive ourselves of the advantages of iron shielding. We were able to arrange things so that the Swiss government put at our disposal a part of its war reserves of iron. It was naturally a lot of work to rebuild entirely the shielding, to remove the old concrete blocks and replace them by bars of iron. There were long discussions, and I was, completely contrary to my usual nature, the biggest pessimist, and constantly asked for two more feet of iron here, and another ten yards of iron plates there, to be absolutely sure that we wouldn't run into background difficulties.

"Then a great many people got involved with the shielding: Ramm, von Dardel, Salmeron . . . especially the proton synchrotron people, who, in this second operation also, sighed a bit at first about the enormous weight that had to be moved, but then built the shielding very effectively, as usual, and on time. It was a good thing that we had given so much thought to it, for the first test at CERN, as well as the experiment at Brookhaven, showed that the shielding was infinitely better than in all previous experiments. After several minor improvements that I made myself in several nights, with the help of a crane driver, the shielding became so good that the entire background was negligible compared to the neutrino intensity."

The construction of better shielding was child's play, however, compared to the efforts to intensify the beam. For a long time a team under Berend Kuiper (Holland) and Günther Plass (Germany) had been working on bending the beam of protons, circulating in the Big Machine, one hundred percent out of the PS, and only then to let the protons hit the target. Up to then, the beams of secondary particles, which the physicists were interested in, had always been generated through collision with a target that had been pushed into the circular path of the protons, that is, a target that was inside the machine. Nine tenths of the particles were lost in the process, however, because they left the machine in such a narrow cone that sizable particle "traps" (bubble chambers, spark chambers, and other detectors) could not be accommodated.

If the proton beam was to be "bent out," however, then magnets were required that would grab, within fractions of millionths of seconds, the bunches of protons racing around the track and send them off their usual course. Two such magnets were required: a "kicker" magnet to supply the first powerful impulse (with a field strength of 3,000 gauss)—it had been designed by Stefan Pichler of Austria—and a second, even stronger claw, the bending magnet, which had to bend completely into the desired direction (with 15,000 gauss) the proton beam that had already been deviated from its path. The numerous technical problems that had to be solved in order to accomplish these feats are described in a whole pile of technical papers. The layman will find more comprehensible the reports of some participants on the very last difficulties that temporarily stood in the way of success. Faissner says, for example:

"It had almost been possible to do the first improved neutrino experiment by the middle or end of May, but a pump had broken. The rapid deviation of the beam is a very difficult problem, technically. In particular, the magnets must be pushed in hydraulically, within a tenth of a second, and then pulled out again. All that with accelerations up to eight times that of gravity, on masses of hundreds of pounds. That required very complicated hydraulics, something the designers were not familiar with—they were electronics and magnet specialists. They had to learn it on the side. The only pump that could maintain the high pressure in this hydraulic system was in the aircraft industry, because high pressure is required for hydraulic landing gear. One firm supplied us with a pump—that developed a crack after a few days, which caused another delay of a few weeks."

Fewer difficulties were caused by a new construction based on an invention by a Dutch CERN member, Simon van der Meer. With the help of his "magnetic horn," the pions could be collected, somewhat like sound in a megaphone, and then transmitted, in concentrated form, into the desired direction. But even here, things didn't work out entirely according to one's wishes, and finally, in order to avoid certain vibrations, at a certain spot in the magic horn a cushion was stuffed in, unofficially. Up to now it has not appeared in any of the published construction designs. Nevertheless, it was indispensable.

IX

Thus, in the first days of June, 1963, the time was just about set for the entire ultrarefined and strengthened experimental setup for CERN's neutrino experiment to be put into readiness for a new series of tests. By then it had cost millions of Swiss francs in manpower, material, and energy. Faissner reports on these last days:

"Things became serious. Once again the schedule was extremely tight. People were rebuilding up until the last second. Jean-Marc Gaillard, our French team member, who had taken part in the Brookhaven experiment, came back with a big magnet in his 'luggage' and announced, 'We have to add another magnet.' That is, he knew that there were still a few large magnet coils lying around from the days when cosmic ray research was being done at the Ecole Polytechnique, and he arranged for us to borrow them. They were quickly brought from Paris by special transport.

"Behind the 'neutrino mountain' was the 'neutrino blockhouse' with much concrete and lots of iron right and left, above and below, where our detectors were located: in front, the bubble chamber; farther back, our large spark chamber and counter

119

system. Since there was not enough room for the magnet at first, the floor had to be ripped up. But these are all things that are done extremely quickly at CERN. Then, the floor was a bit too weak, and when we rolled in the spark chambers, they sank in lopsided and couldn't be moved. They had to be dragged out again, and a special floor put in. But that one was even worse than the first. Finally, we laid some steel plates on the floor, hauled in our spark chambers, adjusted them, made the magnet work, even managed to make the electronic 'photomultipliers,' that are used with scintillation counters, work when the magnet was switched on, even though they are disturbed by the magnet.

"On June 13—Corpus Christi Day—things had gone far enough for the neutrino beam to be started up. We had made good use of the period of waiting caused by the breakdown of the pump. We had been able, with cosmic rays, which, fortunately, are always present, even when the proton synchrotron's pump isn't working, to test our spark chambers very precisely. The apparatus was exact to a few billionths of a second in the synchronization of one counter with the next. All the electronics worked. The probability with which each counter would register a particle had been measured.

"After we were certain we really had the right time within fractions of a millionth of a second, at six o'clock on the evening of June 13, we switched over to neutrino conditions. The test beam that we got from the PS was turned off, and I went to a party that Weisskopf gave at his house. Weisskopf was naturally also very eager to know what would happen and said: 'Everything should be okay now.' Shortly before I left the lab, I had stopped in again, and had looked at the spark chamber, in the dark. It crackled from time to time, and one could see some kind of traces, but it was never entirely clear *what* was actually there. But my confidence in the calculations of Simon van der Meer, my confidence in the ideas of Lee and Yang, and in the apparatus was so great that I told myself, now that I am at the party, the first neutrinos are probably being registered; and that was exactly how things went!

"During the night—I had the early shift—the first films were developed and feverishly analyzed. There were, in fact, the first definite evidences of neutrinos. And then, within a few days of this pre-run that was actually not the experiment proper, the results of Brookhaven were not only confirmed but superseded. Within a few more days we had collected more events than Brookhaven had been able to measure in several months."

X

CERN's big neutrino experiment had yielded many important results, that thus far had not been found by any other laboratory, and which had a strong influence on the further development of this new special branch of nuclear physics, but the intermediate boson was not discovered. That theoretically conjectured particle, the identification of which would shed light on the mysterious field of "weak interactions," despite all endeavors, was not to be seen for the time being, either in Meyrin or in Brookhaven. Hundreds of experimental runs had not been able to furnish the proof of the existence of this particle "W," that had been named before it had been observed and registered. Therefore, after more than a year of intense activity, in which hundreds of people had participated, the biggest experiment the European Laboratory for Nuclear Research had attempted thus far was broken off. It had yielded a number of interesting results, but not the one for which it had been planned. One still hopes, some time in the future, to find this quantum of weak interactions, by using other experimental arrangements, and more powerful machines.

At CERN such disappointments are accepted, not only with composure but perhaps even with a kind of grim joy. When things don't fit, then they first start to get really interesting! This is the attitude of physicists, and with it they pay a compliment to their antagonist, Nature, who is always a little more complex than had been anticipated.

With this experiment as an example, I realized how misleading descriptions of scientific experiments can be. The usual representation of the scientist hurrying from one success to another conveys a false picture, not only to the general public but especially to those young people who want to devote themselves to uncovering the mysteries of nature. What is all too often missing from those reports is the description of the detours, the dead ends, the obliterated tracks. And it is for just these periods of spiritual want, these times of despair, that students must be prepared, or else later they will lack the necessary patience and perseverance.

Perhaps it would be fruitful if scientists published not only their successful experiments—as is done almost without exception—but occasionally their errors and failures as well. That would give a picture of the search for new knowledge that is closer to reality.

FIVE

The
Network

I

Not only are experiments performed at CERN—CERN is itself an experiment. One afternoon, I had a vision of all the lively commotion on the spacious laboratory grounds occurring in a kind of giant bubble chamber, with the people, in their eager actions, playing the role of particles "interacting" with one another in measurable time intervals, transmitting and receiving signals, combining and separating again, regrouping and vanishing.

When people asked me, the outsider, what I was actually doing there when I went around looking and listening, I answered: "Something very similar to what you do. I try to observe new and unusual processes. Most of what I see I cannot yet interpret, some I half understand, and a little I understand quite well. One thing I have learned from you is that a single individual doesn't amount to much in this kind of enterprise. What a marvelous testing ground a research center like this would provide for sociologists and psychologists studying the problems connected with team work and the functioning of large organizations."

It seems to me that a large-scale laboratory of this kind would be especially interesting as a model of a society which, through inventions and innovations, is forced to change continually and to test new relationships between people and between people and their machines. Transitoriness, in this milieu of permanent change, is no longer the result of natural erosion but the consequence of a striving that is never satisfied, a pushing forward impatiently that sees in the greatest achievements of today that which must be discarded tomorrow.

This permanent progress, which forces upon the institution an ever increasing tempo, straining it almost to the breaking point, is more manifest in laboratories like CERN and Brookhaven than in industry, because there is no pressure for amortization. Although an institution devoted to basic research must make good use of the means at its disposal, it does not have to make a profit. Its prime concern, therefore, is not lucrativeness, but maximum scientific productivity, even when the financial sacrifices are great. Each too slow reaction to a promising idea, each hesitation to take up an untried technique, each reluctance to acquire a new apparatus can mean a fall from the top of research, with a consequent gradual decline of the institution. The research race is thus comparable to the armaments race.

At the time CERN was founded, people had not thought about this pressure for dynamism; perhaps, in order not to scare off the governmental financers, they had only refrained from speaking about it. The very precise estimates of the size of the lab and of its future personnel that were made in the trial years always dealt with a rather limited number of employees and a budget as fixed as possible. Therefore, in 1953 it was estimated that the completed and fully equipped laboratory would employ a maximum of 302 persons (including administrative staff, mechanics, and unskilled laborers). For that time it was quite a daring undertaking; no institution in Europe engaged in basic research had ever employed more than one hundred people. But as a matter of fact, in 1960 more than a thousand people were working at Meyrin; in 1963 the number of employees exceeded two thousand; and three years later, as many as twenty-five hundred were counted, including visitors. In January, 1953, a document for internal use, dealing with construction of the laboratory, read: "The premises are so extensive that multistoried buildings are not necessary, even if future needs are taken into account." By 1960, however, these same premises had become too confined, and the supply of water and power inadequate. Also there was a great deal of regret that the style of architecture that the Zurich architect Rudolf Steiger had selected on esthetic grounds, featuring sloping roofs instead of the flat sort customary for this kind of building, made it impossible to add more stories to increase the amount of work space.

John Adams had recognized fully, as early as 1960, immediately after the inauguration of the proton synchrotron, that the laboratory had two possibilities open to it from then on: CERN could—as had been projected—either stop at a certain point in its external development, with a fixed budget and a fixed staff, and make use of the existing research apparatus, or it could continue to expand. It does not speak very well for the powers of prognostication of the founders of CERN that they had not forseen the necessity for maintaining one's place in the research race once one had entered it. However, they were not the only ones to have underestimated, at the beginning of the fifties, the scope and rate of scientific and technological development. Almost no one at that time, so soon after the war, had had enough foresight and optimism properly to evaluate the industrial acceleration that had just begun in some countries.

II

One was equally unprepared for the rapid, radical changes in the working methods of scientists engaged in basic research. When I asked Werner Heisenberg at a conference in Vienna in 1963 for his attitude on large research centers like CERN, he used a family event to illustrate the difference between the manner of doing scientific work in his youth and that of modern times, a difference that had suddenly become obvious. His daughter, he told me, was to have been married on one of these beautiful summer days. But unfortunately nothing came of it. The wedding had to be postponed because his future son-in-law —a physicist, of course—was taking part in an important experiment that couldn't be finished in time. To ask for a vacation, or to take off, even for a few days, was out of the question, as the young man was indispensable to his group; he had "calibrated" instruments necessary for the experiment (that is, checked their accuracy against other instruments) and was responsible for their functioning. His leaving would have been a real blow to his team. On the other hand, an interruption or a postponement of the experiment was not possible, despite the best of intentions, because other teams had months ago reserved all the available "machine time" on the big accelerator.

The situation is a typical one for today's scientist. His life is increasingly determined by his institute's long-term schedule, which is designed to make full use of instruments that run twenty-four hours a day. Besides, he must take into account not only the rhythm of the machines with which he works but also the growing number of others without whose assistance he can no longer accomplish his ends. Like the astronaut in his capsule entering new spheres, he is dependent upon an entire network of people in other occupations. These are specialists, such as geologists, engineers, biologists, electronics engineers, chemists, mathematicians, magnet physicists, health physicists, administrators, personnel managers, and technical purchasing agents, along with construction workers, firemen, mechanics, telephone operators, secretaries, and many others. For quite some time scientists have constituted a very small minority in the laboratory. At the end of 1965 the number of people employed at CERN (not counting visitors from other laboratories) totaled 2,191. Of that number, 922 were listed under "Services and Craftsmen," 316 under "Administration," 604 under "Technicians," and only 349 under "Scientists and Engineers." This last figure must be divided once more in order to arrive at the number of actual nuclear physicists.

The scientist can no longer be regarded as a professional in the former sense of the term. Today, he, too, is an "organization man." True, his is not the usual kind of organization, but one employing a high percentage of thinking, critical minds, and therefore finding it necessary to grant to them a fair amount of say in policy if it wishes to remain active and creative. This kind of work force, including a large number of qualified, self-confident people of high intellectual standards, presumably will be the rule in the world of tomorrow. They will be able to build upon the experiences of pioneer establishments like CERN.

There, the conflicts that exist in every large organization are not hushed up, but are openly discussed and decided; tensions are considered a sign of vitality, criticism an expression of genuine interest. No one tries to instill artificial harmony and false peace in the enterprise. The leadership feels obliged always to state openly the reasons for its decisions. It is also not afraid to admit errors. A prime example of this type of behavior is to be found in the so-called "computer crisis" at CERN, which lasted months.

III

To begin with, CERN could manage with a combination of small data-processing machines and the services of a well-known mathematical prodigy snatched from the vaudeville stage, Willem Klein of Holland, who, despite his phenomenal gifts, finally had to succumb to the computer, with its greater speed and far superior memory. It is generally accepted today that, were it not for the introduction of increasingly larger computers, high-energy physics would have been swamped by the overflow of data from its accelerators. CERN—in particular, the former head of its Data Handling Division, Kowarski, one of the founders of the laboratory—is credited with having foreseen the need as early as the end of the fifties and having put it up for international debate. The idea found immediate approval in the United States, especially in Berkeley, where Luis Alvarez, a physicist known for his remarkable foresight, had been dealing for some time with the flood of data and the possibilities for handling it. From that resulted the joint development of the Hough-Powell Digitizer and the electronic scanning device built in Meyrin, "Luciole," as well as the invention of the PEPR (Precision Encoder and Pattern Recognizer) by Irwin Pless of Massachusetts Institute of Technology.

But full use of these "seeing" instruments, that functioned almost automatically with a minimum of human assistance, could really only be made if they were combined with increasingly faster electronic computers. In 1961 CERN replaced its first computer, which had been installed in 1958, by a larger one. The next step came in 1962-63. Weisskopf had to press very hard to overcome the initial reluctance of the financial supporters of CERN to acquire these expensive new data-processing devices, for only very few at that time were aware of the tremendous importance of the computer in the further development of research in physics. For the moment only a compromise was possible: a single computer, which was really not sufficient for their needs. But in 1963 a seemingly radical proposal was finally pushed through. In an effort to ensure CERN's leading position in the future, the CDC 6600, the most highly developed—but barely tested—computer at that time, was purchased for an enormous sum. The 6600 was flown across the Atlantic and received with great expectations in Cointrin. Confidence in the anticipated performance of this representative of the "new generation" of electronic brains was so great that the old computer was put aside before the new one had proved itself. But for a while, the highly acclaimed instrument did not seem to warrant its praises.

The consternation of the physicists, who got back their calculations from the programmers either after enormous delays, or full of mistakes, was obvious to me even in the appearance of the computing center when I visited it. All over the floor lay discarded, torn, or crumpled punch cards. Broad white strips of paper, the wrong answers of the fallible "oracle," hung out of overflowing wastepaper baskets. In front of the windows where the physicists handed in their problems to the programmers stood groups or lines of angry users. I learned that several impatient users had sat down at the console of the big box, without permission, in order to find out for themselves where and in what state the problems they had fed into the 6600 were to be found. Their interference only served to increase the confusion, however, because other half-finished computations were disturbed or rendered entirely useless. I even heard that one physicist, like a pagan cursing an idol, had punched the new computer with his clenched fist. The story is probably apocryphal, but it typifies the prevailing mood.

The mood lightened, however, in the course of a series of conferences that brought together the users, the leading figures of the Data Handling Division, and engineers flown over from the U.S. firm that had manufactured the instrument. In these conferences the difficulties were discussed in detail and corrective measures jointly decided upon. The disturbed electronic brain was to be subjected to a thorough, four-week examination. Until it could be restored to health, computers within a radius of hundreds of miles would be used to handle the work that was piling up. CERN purchased computer time in Lausanne,

Frankfurt, London, Pisa, Munich, and Paris for the few hours that were not already rented out. Since those were mostly the hours from midnight to 8 A.M., the itinerant physicists and their accompanying programmers led quite an active night life for a while.

In order to still the rumors that were circulating about the reasons for the failure of the big computer, Neil Spoonley, the alert computer manager of Data Handling, started up an internal news bulletin, the CERN *Computer Newsletter,* which appeared at regular intervals and informed the physicists of the latest condition of the "patient."

One might read, for example: "During the last few weeks the computer was working somewhat irregularly, after a short period of reliability. One of the main difficulties seems to be that certain 'bits' of information get lost in the PP memory and cause hang-ups. The reason for these disturbances is not known, and although we have solved the problem partially, at least, it still exists."

Or: "Two new problems have come up. Their effect on the machine is still uncertain, but we are attempting to eliminate them. The grounding of installations in the computer room has become a source of complication due to frequent changes in apparatus . . . giving rise to several disturbances. The second problem is the regulation of climatic conditions. Since the outside air is very dry, the air in the computer room has only 20 percent relative humidity. That can cause trouble if the cases are not well grounded. . . ."

Finally, the manufacturer sent two permanent service engineers to its big box in Meyrin, and arrangements were made for them to work every night from midnight until eight in the morning to "improve" the machine.

In June, 1966, the *Newsletter* was able to announce: "The program for the improvement of the computer is continuing. . . . The control unit and the memory have been tested for loose connections. . . . The temperature of the entire machine has been raised by 10°F. . . . Several metal partitions separating one logic unit from the next were replaced because they were warped. . . . All in all, the program of improvement is going forward and is ahead of schedule. But there are still some unexplained phenomena in parts of the machine that have not yet been examined. . . . Two or three times the machine was returned to use late, because the repair work itself had introduced new sources of error. . . . The total amount of time lost in this way has been twenty-five hours in three weeks. . . ."

With the active cooperation of CERN's programmers, who developed a special language for the new instrument, the CDC 6600 was gradually nursed back to health. To help out in the interim, the manufacturer had sent a somewhat smaller computer to Meyrin, the CDC 3400. There were soon difficulties with that one, too. The *Newsletter* reported: "CDC has an engineer here supervising the 3400. . . . One Saturday, recently, when the engineer was away, the machine began to give wild answers. The engineer could not be got hold of until Monday morning. But at that time no fault whatever could be found with the machine. It was working completely normally once more."

"How do you explain that?" I asked one of the programmers, who had risen from fireman to data specialist.

"It's clear," he said; "even a computer wants a weekend off once in a while."

IV

At CERN, even wage conflicts are decided publicly, and, it goes without saying, in a scientific manner. I attended a meeting in the overcrowded main auditorium in which the personnel association presented its demands for salary increases. The whole thing was conducted like a seminar. First a speaker representing the employees gave a lecture. To support his claims, he illustrated his talk with slides of curves and statistical plots. The administrative director replied with complicated mathematical formulae expressing the relation between salaries paid in the laboratory and the increase in the cost of living and wage scales in other organizations. An opposing speaker tried to show that these calculations were not sufficiently objective, because certain factors had not been taken properly into account. Naturally, he was quick to use chalk to write his blackboard calculations. Arguments went back and forth in this way for quite a while. They were so serious and thorough (and, for the non-mathematician, almost incomprehensible) that it was as though a new branch of science were under discussion: the physics of salaries.

Even livelier are the committee meetings, in which decisions are made on initiating new experiments or continuing those already in progress. (CERN has a Track Chamber Committee, an Electronic Experiments Committee, a Nuclear Emulsion Experiments Committee, and, over them, the Nuclear Physics Research Committee.) The necessity for making use of the financial and technical resources of the laboratory as judiciously as possible, and for allocating the ever-too-short time on the Big Machine and the computers justly, leads, not seldom, to differences of opinion. Applicants attempt to convince their colleagues that a trace or an assumption that they wish to investigate further might yield pay dirt. Critics protest and propose other schemes. These debates are conducted in a restrained manner, but, even here, a good speaker can win out even if the facts are not on his side. A man who is able to talk in a convincing manner about things that are not yet clearly established can sometimes come out better than someone else who presents his proposal less eloquently, even though the second might be the more interesting proposal. That is one of the many instances when the highest authorities, the Director-General or the Scientific Council, can intervene to readjust matters.

Experiments in nuclear physics have become so large in scope, so complex and expensive these days, that they can no longer be improvised. The costs may, as in the case of the neutrino experiment, run into millions, the number of man hours and machine shifts into thousands. "In the old days it was simpler," reminisced Fritz Houtermans, one of the most imaginative physicists of the Göttingen generation. "Then, if someone had a crazy idea (and, according to Niels Bohr, they are the salt of physics), he would disappear from the scene and shut himself up in the laboratory for a few days. Nowadays every experiment starts with the writing of applications and the drawing up of estimates. A lot of the fun and surprise is taken out of physics that way."

Gentner also criticizes the selection procedure, but he sees no alternative to it today: "It can be argued, for instance, that Roentgen could not have made his discovery if he had been part of an organization, because the experiment that led to his discovery of X rays would never have been accepted by a selection committee. He would not have been able to give good reasons for doing it, nor would any of the 'wise men' have had sufficient imagination to believe in the possibility of rays that penetrate matter. The filtering action that these committees perform carries with it the danger that research is done only in a few selected fields, while other fields remain completely neglected."

The decision-making committees of large laboratories are fully aware of the contradiction between the planning of research work, necessary for technical and economic reasons, and the unpredictability of the truly new, the unexpected, the unexpectable. At the root of all planning is the element of fear of the unknown that throws confusion into arrangements. But meeting with a surprise should not be shunned in science, it should even be sought; it is here that restriction to projects, the success of which is assured from the outset, leads to stagnation in the long run.

This realization has resulted, in recent years, in a pronounced tendency, within the framework of Big Science, to set aside a part of the available funds for far-out projects, and to give not only regulars the opportunity to experiment but some outsiders as well, even at the risk of these detours leading to dead ends. One of the "wise men" Gentner had mentioned described a most gifted CERN member in the following words: "A few hundred years ago, R. would have been a pirate, perhaps, or a circumnavigator of the globe. He is the eternal adventurer described in books. We need him very much, we cherish him even, for he imparts an element of spiritual daring, that seems to me to be indispensable to the 'mixture' in such a large institution."

V

The opposing views of those who press for planning and regulation in a research center, and those who demand a maximum of spontaneity and flexibility will never be reconciled completely, for when different professional groups work together, each is "right" from its point of view. The irritation of the foreman in a machine shop, who complains that he constantly has to grant overtime or bonuses because the physicists refuse to become accustomed to submitting their designs in time, is as understandable as the claim of the scientists that their requirements cannot be foretold in most cases, but come up only as they work. Their complaints, on the other hand, are directed mostly at the bureaucrats who, in reality, ask of them a minimum amount of bookkeeping. The scientists never cease to groan about the red tape and the long hours spent in committee meetings that rob them of precious time for their own work.

The clash of different claims within such a community is expressed particularly well in a statement by Pierre Germain, long-time head of the Big Machine, in which he describes the "natural contrast" between the physicists who make use of apparatus and the technicians who operate it:

"The user wants his experiment to be done as quickly as possible and under the best possible conditions. First, he wants to know the scientific results of his experiment as soon as possible. Second, his achievements are not expected to occur at regular intervals, but in spurts; therefore, it is easy for him to work at an unusual pace. Seen from the viewpoint of the machine personnel, things appear in an entirely different light. To the machine physicist or mechanic this experiment is simply one of many. He will be intent on ordering the different jobs in the proper sequence, and, in the interest of everyone concerned, will try to arrive at the maximum output with the greatest efficiency. He is, unfortunately, more familiar with the limitations of his machine and the technical equipment in the experimental halls. And finally: he cannot afford to work at an abnormal pace, and will hardly ever be able to summon sufficient enthusiasm to allow himself to accept unusual work schedules. One might compare the experimenter to a sprinter, engineers and machine technicians to long-distance runners. . . ."

Germain has enough insight to recognize that both attitudes can be justified. The self-centered enthusiasm of the scientist on the one hand, and the tendency to systematize of the machine personnel on the other, continually have to be brought into equilibrium, therefore, by way of understanding and concession, first from one side, then from the other.

Another source of tension between service personnel and scientists is more difficult to eradicate. Physicists are permitted to do research at CERN for a limited time only, as a rule, in order to give members of as many institutes as possible the opportunity to work at this top laboratory. Thus, eighty percent of the scientists at Meyrin are only "visitors" or "fellows," who stay no longer than two years. Of the remaining twenty percent, the "staff," most have contracts for only three or six years. Very few scientists have permanent positions. Qualified machine physicists and mechanics, however, often hold lifetime positions.

"We can't manage it any other way," said Weisskopf. "Ten years ago it was still easy to attract good engineers to Geneva. Today European industry is highly developed, and it is much harder to get technical personnel of first quality because, although CERN holds interest for them, it is not unique, while for a high-energy physicist it is unique. That leads to some injustice toward the physicists. 'Why can *they* stay in Geneva and not us? We have to leave even though we have higher positions,' they complain."

In words like these, the nuclear scientists exhibit a kind of arrogance, which is at the bottom of certain personal difficulties in the lab. The physicists are aware that they are the elite of the institute, and let others know it, often only too clearly. They are reproached for not properly appreciating the arduous and highly creative work of the machine physicists, "beam makers," high-frequency engineers, electronics specialists, programmers, and all the other people on whom they depend so much. "In their eyes we're only blacksmiths. They look upon us as lower class," is an often heard complaint. Or: "These conceited gentlemen don't even bother to explain to us why the experiment is actually being done, when we're taking part in it as much as they are. The reason they give? That is much too difficult to explain to the uninitiated. But when for once an informed person goes to the trouble of giving introductory lectures to the personnel on the problems of nuclear physics, as Dr. Rafael Carreras did, for example, they don't like that either. They ridicule and turn up their noses at these attempts to improve communication in the lab."

Only a few scientists are exempt from this charge of arrogance. Usually they are the most outstanding of the scientists. They express themselves like normal human beings, is the claim, while the average scientist does not even want to be understood.

This hubris seems especially widespread among the younger physicists who, because of increasingly higher specialization and greater division of labor, no longer have as close ties to the engineers and mechanics who assist them as do the older physicists who once handled experimental apparatus themselves. The younger ones take for granted the fact that research instruments are built for them by others, and then are operated by still others. Their confidence in technical aids with structures and designs that are often unfamiliar is high. They have grown up in a world accustomed to almost undisturbed functioning of astonishing, often invisible systems of technical supply and distribution. They use the modern, highly developed instruments available to them in the research institutes as naturally as they use the telephone. The lack of contact then inclines them to make almost impossible demands on the supporting staff of machine physicists and technicians. In the engineers' eyes, these physicists are fussy, irresponsible, and unrealistic pushers. "Just look at that guy over there," one of the machine physicists said to me, pointing to someone hobbling by on crutches. "A skiing accident! Naturally, an experimental physicist. They always think they will achieve more than they actually can."

VI

The tensions in a large laboratory, touched upon here, that can occasionally develop into power struggles between individual groups, indicate how difficult the job of the director of the institution must be. As long as the laboratory can still be overseen and the leader not only knows everyone but is also available to everyone without difficulty, conflicts can be solved more easily than in an enterprise with a thousand or more employees. In the latter, the head is forced more and more to use written directives. The lines of communication from the employees to him and from him to the employees must be subject to regulations and, therefore, must be more formal than in a smaller research center.

"I actually envy you a little, because you can wander around here freely, can see everything, hear everything," were the words with which Director-General Weisskopf once received me in his office. I got the impression that he felt cut off from the real life of the laboratory because of his exalted position. Although it was commonly known that anyone could approach him with his desires or complaints, only a few resorted to it.

"Why don't you go to him directly?" I asked someone who had requested that I pass on one of his proposals to the director.

"I can't," he said. "Every one of my colleagues would know about it the very next day, and then I'd really be in a fix."

In any case, I noticed that there was one way, at least, of talking to the DG (Director-General) without attracting special attention. Weisskopf usually went to lunch in the large cafeteria, where everybody had to get on line for food and sit together at long tables. There, he could engage in conversations *en passant*, could listen to suggestions, learn people's wishes and give advice.

The more I saw of the "social experiment," CERN, the greater became my admiration for the DG. Just as Adams had been the builder of the Big Machine, Weisskopf was the spiritual builder of the lab. He had, in repeated efforts, united hundreds of divergent personalities from widely varying occupations into a living and growing whole. Certainly there was obstinacy and ambition at CERN, as there is everywhere where people live together, but *l'esprit du* CERN, a spirit of tolerance and freedom, always triumphed in the end.

I asked Weisskopf how he had accomplished that feat, and out of modesty he refused at first to answer. When I pressed him, he thought that perhaps it was because he had brought with him from his native Vienna a certain atmosphere of *Gemütlichkeit* and from the United States a respect for the opinions of others.

In addition to a tremendous amount of praise for the DG, I also heard criticism, of course, in the lab. In the main it was a question of the boss holding the reins too loosely. But after visiting Brookhaven and Dubna, the other two great laboratories for nuclear research, I discovered that it was this very self-restraint on the part of the director that was responsible for the incomparably better atmosphere at CERN. Weisskopf is of the opinion that a director should not "cast his shadow" over a large-scale scientific enterprise. He refrained, therefore, from making authoritarian decisions in conflicts, although often it might have saved time. In a community of thinking and knowing people this kind of understanding, mediating attitude has very much more effect in the long run than the rule of a "strong man," whose decisions may sometimes bring more clarity, but with it more friction and hidden opposition or—even worse—resigned submission.

VII

It was on the testing ground of CERN that I learned that tensions in a community should not be eliminated but should be redirected into producing energy. An example of this is to be seen in the excessive demands that are constantly being made on the technical resources by the nuclear scientists. They have the effect of a challenge to which the immediate reaction often is "Impossible!" or "Madness!" but which eventually leads to the possible and the reasonable.

Perhaps that is why the relationship to the machines of those who must deal with them is better in institutions like CERN than in industrial plants. Apparatus are not considered rigid or tyrannical, but as creations that are never entirely finished, always still imperfect, and therefore always subject to the will of the person who works with them. For that reason, a Soviet scientist told me, he and his co-workers often actually preferred the imprecise, badly functioning instruments they received from factories to devices that work perfectly immediately. "We play around with them until we bring them up to the level of operation we want," he said. "Then they aren't strange to us any more. They belong to our team in a very special way. We have 'educated' them."

At CERN, too, no instrument is left in the state in which it arrived from the manufacturer. It must by all means be "improved," even when it works satisfactorily. Thus, the European Council for Nuclear Research has, on the side, simultaneously become a European institution for the continuous invention and improvement of new technical devices. True, the experiments of the nuclear physicists are at the core of all efforts, but there are always a number of peripheral experiments going on, devoted to the development of more precise and more powerful instruments. Some physicists hold that this constant effort to improve research mechanisms has gone too far, however. It has in their opinion gradually become an end in itself and has started to force the true goals of research into the background.

The results of the improvements are highly impressive. The proton synchrotron, after several years of "education" and "refinement," differs as much from the PS inaugurated at the end of 1959 as a man in the prime of life does from a youth fresh out of school. The adult PS can simply "do" more than when it came into the world. Its dexterity has grown, its skills have been refined. Its intensity—that is, the number of protons dispatched to the target with each pulse—has increased a hundredfold. According to statements made by machine physicists, the peak has not yet been reached.

The art of "beam sharing," in particular, was developed during the years in which practical experience in the use of the new instrument was being gained. Beam sharing makes it possible for up to nine teams to work simultaneously on the Big Machine. On the machine coordinator's desk there always lies a schedule for a ten-day period, and, next to it, a multicolored ground plan of the PS. The latter indicates clearly the different directions the beams take from the circle of magnets of the synchrotron out to the halls, an arterial system that, pulsating regularly, transmits the flux of particles from the accelerator to the detectors of the various research groups. On beam d_{15}, "supplying" pions that come off sideways from "target number 1," is Hyams's group, interested in the study of gamma rays. Nearby, still in the South Hall, is the group under Zichichi, on beam m_4, observing the pairs of muons expected to result from the collision of protons with antiprotons. Group q_3, headed by Giuseppe Fidecaro of Italy, hopes to gain further information about the new, recently discovered particle "rho." In addition, beam c_8 is being directed into the North Hall for experiment S 24, and beam a_8 is being used for a "cooperation" among the institutes of Bristol, Lausanne, Munich, and Rome.

If one were to view in a somewhat different way this minutely planned, complicated arrangement, its creation, its existence, and finally its alterations, one would find Pierre Bertaux's prophecy of a future symbiosis between groups of humans and the machines they create confirmed here and now.

VIII

The physicists who band together to form a team, one time for one experiment, another time for several, make up a special type of community. There are conflicts within it, of course, but the ties of common experience and common achievement, which can only be hinted at to the outside world, are uncommonly strong. The American physicist and philosopher Gerald Holton finds the typical scientist of today "much more his own constantly changing creation than is true of any other ordinary human being." For him, because of the whirlwind development of his field, not even the most recent past can point the direction of the future. It has already become "prehistory." Therefore, he must rely exclusively upon his own abilities and on those of his scientific contemporaries.

This uniting feeling of "contemporariness" stems, as Holton has explained, above all, from experiencing jointly a reality that does not conform to the reality that others know, for it is infinitely more complicated, more contradictory, and consequently more magnificent than the structure of the macroscopic world around us that is grasped by one's senses and one's "common sense." The fact that this other deeper layer cannot be imagined or expressed in ordinary language, establishes bonds among physicists, which are known elsewhere only in occult sects. But their modern arcana are not hidden; they are published openly. Despite that, they remain secret to all but the lucky few. That strengthens the togetherness of the physicists even more, since each of them is proud of having been admitted to the mystery not through an act of favor, but as a reward for intellectual achievement. The research group is united by a feeling of camaraderie, and, in some instances, by the kind of enthusiasm that a group of mountaineers, roped together, experiences on a pioneer ascent.

In a team of this type a person feels that he is not among equals but among similars, with each one having his own particular forte in a different area. The group leader will be careful not to act dictatorially or even autocratically, for his co-workers have awarded him his position of leadership only temporarily in most cases, be it because he was the first to think of a certain experiment, or because he has greater perspective, or simply because he is a better manager. In another experiment the make-up of the group might be altered, with the leader and the led interchanged.

It is commonly held that in basic research a scientist's best years are those between twenty and thirty, a verity that often leads to situations today that would hardly be tenable on the outside, that is, in the world outside the laboratory. The older, more experienced scientist steps back in favor of a younger, because he acknowledges the latter's greater propensity for "radical thinking" and his greater familiarity with the latest developments. Even Hans Bethe, one of the most outstanding figures in modern physics, who, like many other masters of the trade, spent several weeks at CERN, told me with a resigned smile that he sometimes found it hard to keep up with the best of the young people—one probably had to be in his twenties in order to maintain the pace.

How quickly even the most advanced physical knowledge becomes outdated today is indicated by the fact that in the American journal *Physical Review Letters*, which specializes in publishing original scientific papers with great rapidity, half of the references cited by authors are less than two and one half years old. Publications going back five or ten years are considered worth mentioning only in exceptional cases.

It is remarkable how most of the older generation accept the situation. In the division of labor, they voluntarily take upon themselves those administrative and representational duties that seem to be more of a chore to the younger scientists in the most productive phase of their careers. On the other hand, the question arises whether, in view of the pronounced increase in the number of physicists in the last few years, all the "old ones"—and "being old" begins, at the latest, at forty—will, later, still be able to find the positions they merit.

The gloomy forecast of the professional opportunities for the older scientist, which has been expressed only very infrequently up to now (by the sociologist Hans-Paul Bahrdt, of Göttingen, for example) is only one of the many unsolved problems resulting from research having become a "mass undertaking." Today, science is no longer a profession restricted to an elite; it has become a job like any other. It attracts intelligent young people because it has prestige associated with it, promises to be interesting, and offers in most countries (but by no means in all) high salaries and social status.

How can a "born scientist" or an especially gifted one still be distinguished from the others? Exceptionally brilliant minds will always stand out, but what about the rest? The list of authors on a scientific publication emerging from a CERN experiment looks like the following: Jauneau, L.; Morellet, D.; Nguyen-Khac, U.; Rousset, A.; Six, J.; Bingham, H. H.; Koch, W.; Nikolié, M.; Ronne, B.; Skjeggestad, O.; Sletten, H.; Common, A. K.; Esten, M. J.; Henderson, C.; Fisher, C. M.; Scarr, J. M.; Thomas, R. H.; Haatuft, A.; Millerud, R.; Myklebost, K.

Twenty co-authors appearing on a single publication of a few printed pages is no longer unusual. True, there are more publications with "only" four to eight authors, but there are others that cite up to fifty-one! Scientific papers with only one or two authors become rarer every year. The American historian Derek J. de Solla Price feels that he can predict the complete disappearance of individual scientific endeavor, for experiments of necessity are becoming more complex and the specialists taking part in them more numerous.

Does it make sense then, when faced with such an aggregate of names, to list every single participant as an author? Does the list in fact include the names of every single participant in the experiment? That is not at all certain. Often the sources of the ideas can no longer be isolated from the flood of technical discussions in a modern institution. When Gentner asked who had actually worked on the important G-2 experiment at CERN, he received the following answer:

"Well, after two years of work, that can no longer be stated so exactly. Some of the participants were visitors from the United States who stayed only half a year. The composition of the group changed frequently. As far as I know, the idea for the experiment came out of a discussion in X's room. But with regard to who was the first to express it, we couldn't decide afterward. So we just listed as authors all the participants of the last two years, in alphabetical order."

The problem of the proper assignment of credits on scientific publications has been under discussion for years, and has occupied the thoughts of many at CERN. Perhaps the best thing would be to cease mentioning individuals altogether, and to cite only the name of the entire laboratory. That would be considerably more just, for then the machine physicists, electronics specialists, and mechanics would also be included, and they often play a more important role in setting up the experiment than some of those whose names eventually appear on the publication. Since for each physicist who works on an experiment there are half a dozen technicians on the average, hundreds of people are involved in a single experiment.

For these various reasons, serious discussions were conducted at CERN on radical reform of the system for allocating credit. Reform was instituted only once, and then abandoned, because almost every experiment includes a number of foreign visitors and fellows who are only temporarily members of CERN, the collective author. Yet these visitors would like—indeed *must have* —documentation for the experiments they have worked on, for the scientific public. It is by no means dictated by vanity, but by common practice in today's "academic market," where a scientist's worth is assessed largely by the number of publications he has to his credit.

When a great many individual names are cited, the question of what order inevitably arises. An alphabetical listing would be highly unjust, because seldom are more than the first two or three names mentioned in references, the remaining participants being forced to content themselves with the designation *"et al.,"* and thus it might happen that the names of those most responsible for the success of the experiment would not appear.

Therefore, one tries in most cases to list the names in order of importance. That can be done without argument in many cases. One usually knows which theoretician suggested the experiment; which experimenter thought up the right apparatus; who, in a crisis, had the idea that saved the day. But certainly, equally often an order according to merit is less straightforward. Then, in the attempt to evaluate individual contributions, a disturbing element of rivalry is introduced into a group that has often worked together in friendship, day and night, for years, a rivalry that is in strong contrast to the spirit of joint effort.

Wolfgang Gentner states in the article quoted earlier:

"For a laboratory to be successful, its scientists must not only be capable, but must also possess a good team spirit; they must be interested in the problems of modern physics in themselves, and must enjoy the cooperation involved in their solution. People with strong personal ambitions will find no friends there. . . . The individual must derive his satisfaction from the joy of sharing in the erecting of the magnificent edifice that is the laws of Nature. Who can still name the members and founders of the guilds that built the great cathedrals of the Middle Ages, such as those at Strassburg and Freiburg? Hardly any names have been handed down. For them it was enough to have worked on these masterpieces."

Such words, in my opinion, express more wishful thinking than reality for the moment. Certainly at CERN there is a tendency for the individual to step back in favor of the group, but in these times that are ruled by the spirit of competition, in contrast to the era described by Gentner, even the scientist working in a research center cannot remain aloof from the rat race. If a scientist were able to work at CERN throughout his entire career, it might perhaps be possible for him to abjure personal ambition. But only very few become members of the permanent staff. The others must make a name for themselves during the time they can spend at Meyrin, so that they can then secure a good job on the outside, at a university, another research institution, or in industry. One must not be misled by the outward appearances of a modesty bordering almost on self-abnegation, which is required of scientists, into overlooking the bitterness of the struggle for personal prestige forced upon them by circumstances. There is also the fact that the scientist does not make his home in the laboratory but instead, after his workday is done, returns to the outside world in which personal success is the measure of a man. Only a very few strong-minded people can completely withstand this influence.

One still has reservations that CERN will achieve the ideal, though it is beginning to show signs of the community spirit that Gentner envisions. They are partly of an informal nature, such as, for instance, the arrangement made by some teams to stress first one name, then another, in turn, so that each member can be assigned his correct individual market value on the international stock exchange of scholars. There are other, institutional restrictions, however, such as the stipulation that no patents can be filed on inventions or processes developed at CERN. In this way some conflicts that might possibly arise are eliminated at the outset.

But as long as the competitive spirit of the times does not undergo a decided change, the struggle for priority, which has already disrupted partnerships of many years and lifelong friendships among scientists, will not cease.

SIX

The
Planetarians

I

I happened to be going by when an East Berliner took aside a man from Aachen: "It's too early now. At three A.M. here. We'll look through the material again." This exchange in CERN's computing center, suggestive of arrangements for a secret agents' rendezvous, was actually only a harmless conversation between physicists forced by political destiny to live in two separate parts of the same country, each part virtually sealed off from the other. At CERN not only can they speak to one another freely but can even work together on experiments. For within the confines of the European nuclear research center cooperative work between scientists from both sides of the "wall" has never been interrupted, even in times of crisis.

148

In this particular case, members of the Institute of Zeuthen (German Democratic Republic) and of the Technische Hochschule Aachen (Federal Republic of Germany) were working together on an experiment involving the study of the "interactions of high-energy pions and protons." The photographic data had been supplied by the "hydrogen bubble chamber" that had been brought to Meyrin from England. Also participating in the experiment were bubble chamber groups from Cambridge, Hamburg, Cracow, Prague, Stockholm, Vienna, and Warsaw. Teams with this colorful a composition are not at all uncommon. With CERN as an intermediary, scientists from countries widely separated by distance or ideology join together in "cooperations." Experiment E 45 ("Proton Bombardment with a Magnetic Field of 200,000 Gauss") for instance, one of CERN's most successful experiments based on tracks in photographic emulsions exposed at Meyrin, was jointly planned and carried out by institutes in Valencia, Moscow, New Delhi, and Alma Ata. It is taken for granted that there can be close collaboration between scientists from Franco's Spain and scientists from Soviet Russia, between Mongols and Indians.

The creation of CERN helped form the "first Europeans." The lab was not made a scientific "Festung Europa," but an open house that for years has been host to members and visitors from all over the world. The apprehensions of Joliot-Curie, who had opposed its establishment on the grounds that it would pave the way for a "NATO of nuclear physics" that was counter to the international spirit of science, have not been confirmed. In 1965 alone, more than three and one half million bubble chamber photographs went out of Meyrin to thirty-seven institutes all over the globe. Numerous scientists from north and south, east and west, are in constant touch with CERN. In order to set their ship afloat, the founders of the Conseil Européen pour la Recherche Nucléaire, soon after the end of the war, caught the wind from the "European Movement" blowing from an Occidental direction. They then proceeded to steer completely in their own way, disregarding any influence that might have put them on a prescribed course. CERN might today well be the place where one can find the "first Planetarians," earth dwellers who no longer feel loyalty to a single nation, a single continent, or a single political creed, but to the common knowledge that they advance together. The results put forth for discussion by CERN are expressed in a universal language and are based on principles that can be accepted by Europeans as well as Africans, Asians as well as Americans, Marxists as well as non-Marxists.

The partial network that each individual laboratory comprises is connected through its best minds to the larger, earth-spanning network of research and technology which it "supplies" with new results and designs. In return, it receives information on the achievements of other partial networks. Thus a huge, living, pulsating planetary structure takes shape, which gradually pushes through private, national, and ideological walls and exposes their arbitrariness. When I asked CERN members whether their work was impeded by political conflicts, they answered that I was still concerned with problems that for them had long since ceased to exist.

"When someone new arrives, we don't care about his nationality or his ideology, but which lab he came from," I was told. "That is what really interests us. Look, that fellow over there is a Frenchman. But he did his most important work in the United States. Therefore, to us he is a Brookhaven man. And the Englishman next to him is really a Frascati man because he came to us from that Italian research center."

"That's right," agreed Vitali Kaftanov of the Soviet Union, joining the conversation. "Our differences and rivalries are not what they used to be. My friend Hajime Yoshiki here is not first and foremost a Japanese to me, but a member of Ramm's bubble chamber team. I myself belong to these spark chamber people. You know, just because we're all physicists doesn't mean we all have to be pals."

When the banter released by this remark had come to an

end, a German summed up "this obsolete subject": "At CERN we don't even feel like internationalists, for that would presuppose a residue of nationalism. We are simply non-national. Will your generation ever be able to understand that?"

II

In a statement made before the Joint Committee on Atomic Energy of the United States Congress in 1965, Victor Weisskopf distinguished five forms of international cooperation in high-energy physics that had crystallized since the end of the war:

(1) The organization of international conferences and other means of exchange of scientific information, including short-term visits by scientists to other countries.

(2) Longer-term visits by individual scientists, leading to the systematic participation of foreign teams in experiments, with or without the use of apparatus brought along by the foreign team.

(3) A common intercontinental effort to plan experimental research programs for the different existing laboratories.

(4) A common intercontinental effort to plan and coordinate the construction of new accelerators in different countries.

(5) The construction of an intercontinental accelerator jointly owned and operated.

CERN plays a considerable part in all of these attempts to strengthen international science. Meyrin has become one of the central meeting points for physicists from every continent. Hardly a nuclear physicist from abroad fails to stop off in Geneva, when traveling in Europe, to engage in discussions at the European nuclear research center, obtain information, and report privately or in a lecture on the work done in his institute. When the Track Chamber Committee has its monthly meeting, for example, during which international distribution of bubble chamber pictures and applications for experiments submitted by the different "cooperations" are considered, members representing often more than twenty different institutes and almost as many countries are present.

It is regarded as especially fortunate that the Geneva airport is so close to CERN. Foreign visitors are able, therefore, to come to Meyrin for very short visits, often for only a few hours. There had been a complete re-evaluation of distances to other cities at CERN. Places offering good air communications, such as Munich, Nice, and Milan, are "nearer" than the neighboring city of Lyon, because the latter can be reached only by car or train and therefore the journey takes longer.

There was fear at first (especially in Great Britain) that the attractions of a European laboratory might be so great that the universities in the member states would in a short time be left only with people in the second rank. But just the opposite occurred. The national institutions were not left desolate. Instead, with the founding of CERN they began to flourish, inasmuch as scientists returning from Meyrin made efforts to raise the standards of work in their own countries to the higher international level. Then too, most governments realized that physics institutes in the individual countries would be able to make full use of the facilities of a European "top laboratory" only when they had correspondingly advanced equipment of their own.

CERN does not look upon itself as a magnet that attracts the best physicists in order to keep them, but as a kind of "big pump" in the circulatory system of research that sucks in the scientist for a short time to increase his knowledge and skills, and then sends him back into circulation.

The internationality of CERN is of particular advantage in the development of its administrative structure. While most research institutions in the member states had to conform to existing university or government regulations, CERN was not bound by outdated national traditions. It could take over from everywhere those features that were most suitable, or it could establish its own standards and traditions.

152

John Adams points out that one practice evolved at CERN is inevitably a source of concern to outsiders. It is that the sessions of the Conseil, where the highest representatives of the member states debate institute problems, are open to the public. The openness, however, enables the laboratory personnel to get to know all the members of the governing board personally.

CERN's most significant departure from the practices of other international organizations might well be dispensing with the system of distributing the leading positions so that each country would be represented in turn. In the filling of a position, it is in the first place not the nationality of a candidate but his ability that counts. This fact has made it possible twice already for scientists not even belonging to any of the CERN member states to hold the highest office in the organization. Although Bloch and Weisskopf were European by birth, they were naturalized Americans. The freedom from pressure from any of the member states extends to all laboratory acquisitions. Bids are made in open competition and orders are placed according to quality and value, and not simply because it is the "turn" of the industry of some member country.

Language conflicts have been avoided in much the same spirit. With the exception of some publications and directives that are written in two languages (English and French), English is used most. That is not because the Anglo-Saxons have a particularly strong political influence but because, since 1933, English has displaced German as the international language of physics, and even Italians, Indians, Russians, and Chinese publish papers in English in their own journals. John Adams made an interesting observation on the language problem. He maintains that, in his experience, the variety of the tongues at CERN is more a help than a hindrance, for the inability to make cutting remarks in a foreign language mitigates the tensions that come to the surface once in a while in a research institute.

I noticed that very often a conversation at CERN is held in at least three languages. People constantly switch from English to

German, from German to French, and back again to English, hardly noticing the transitions. They have developed their own language, incidentally—"CERNOIS," a mixture of the most important European languages, with technical terms from nuclear physics, accelerator technology, and electronics interspersed, which is very hard, if not impossible, for an outsider to understand. Only when definite instructions are to be given to the technical staff must one's tone and wording be adjusted to the nationality of the person being addressed. George Konried, a British citizen originally from Austria, long-time head of the machine shops at CERN, related to me, from his experience: "If I want something from an Englishman, I need only say 'I would be glad if you could do this or that.' If I said the same thing in the same tone to a Frenchman, he wouldn't take it seriously."

III

People joke about the fact that most nuclear physicists are never to be found in their home laboratories, but "just happen" to be visiting another lab. It is actually true that the traditional inclination of physicists toward personal international contact has become more pronounced since the end of the war. The discussions, meetings, seminars, and conferences become more and more numerous, the distances covered greater and greater. Professor Gentner illustrates the phenomenon pointedly from his own experience, in his classic study:

"Physicists jet from one conference to the next, from Moscow and Tokyo back again to Europe or Australia. Why this haste and frantic unrest that is ordinarily scorned as the enemy of scientific endeavor? Well, because every physicist wants to learn what his colleague thinks of this or that problem directly from him. The development of experimental apparatus is so rapid that there is hardly ever time to describe it properly. Therefore one travels in order to see it with one's own eyes. If one boards a plane that takes the polar route, one can be certain of meeting other physicists hurrying to another 'symposium'—a euphemism for this kind of lightning conference. . . . The end of the symposium leads to a discussion of how one might have a more meaningful exchange next time without being pressed for time. The customary remedy is a splitting into two or more symposia, with its consequent immediate booking of two new flights for next year to different continents, for otherwise one cannot keep abreast of the latest developments."

The young people, who know no other way, accept Big Science, with its many international conferences and symposia, its global hustle and bustle, as a matter of course. When the representative of a research team is to speak at a conference in another part of the world on the work he and his colleagues have done, and telephones his laboratory thousands of miles away shortly before giving his talk, possibly in order to include their very latest results, a fifty-year-old physicist might be shocked at the extravagance, while a twenty- to thirty-year-old will not think much of it at all. The latter asks himself: "Why shouldn't urgent communications in the field of science (which, after all, paved the way for the technology of global communication) be at least as important as the latest sports news? And why shouldn't scientists, too, take advantage of the fact that in today's world the most important centers are only a few plane hours apart?" Reines and his co-workers, for example, have been flying back and forth constantly between New York and Capetown since 1964, because their "traps" for capturing neutrinos from cosmic radiation are located deep in a South African gold mine. For them the jet plane is almost like a commuter train, the main difference being the fare—and that is not paid by the scientist but by his laboratory.

The main incentive for the planetary mobility of scientists is the hope of getting firsthand information on the most recent of the recent developments in their own specialities, rather than having to wait until the scientific results appear in print—because by then it is mostly old stuff to the initiated. If one wants to be in the top group in science, he must receive information as quickly as does a stockbroker, in order not to invest the energies and resources of his lab in an experiment that might possibly have been in the planning stage for some time elsewhere, or has even been started. In addition, it is a way of letting one's "competitors" know what his next project will be, and thereby staking out a claim on a particular problem. If one should learn that the investigations of other groups into the same area have advanced to a comparable degree, he may attempt, on behalf of his team, to establish an alliance and consider concerted effort.

This need for frequent personal contact and discussion is intensified by the increasing abundance of scientific publications from all over the world, which threatens to get out of hand. Of the 600,000 scientific papers that are now being published each year, according to the figures of Derek J. de Solla Price, the expert must mainly be acquainted with those in his own specialty and in some related fields; however, even those amount to hundreds or thousands. The rapid separation of the essential from the nonessential is done best by those belonging to the top group in a particular field. An elite of this kind admits into its small circle only those scientists who have attracted attention through some outstanding work.

Price is of the opinion that such informal elite groups of, on the average, one hundred eminent scholars, selected from a population of tens of thousands, are coming into existence in all research fields, particularly the newer ones. Through preprints they send one another private communications in letters, telephone calls, and telegrams, but especially through frequent personal encounters, they form their own international and intercontinental communication system. "They seem to have mastered the art of attracting invitations from centers where they can work along with several members of the group for a short time," Price writes, in *Little Science, Big Science*. "This done, they move on to the next center and other members. . . . Such groups constitute an invisible college. . . . They give each man status in the form of approbation from his peers, they confer prestige, and, above all, they effectively solve a communication crisis by reducing a large group to a small select one of the maximum size that can be handled by interpersonal relationships. . . . Although a place such as Brookhaven [or Meyrin!] was once where one went to work with Big Machines and certain other facilities, it has come nowadays to play an increasingly important role as a station on the commuting circuit of several invisible colleges. People come to work with other people, who have come to work with yet other people, who happen to be there."

IV

It is especially interesting to trace how the isolated nuclear scientists in the socialist camp gradually established contact with the worldwide network of scientists, in the first ten years after the war.

Several months after Stalin's death in the spring of 1953, the scientific exchange between the institutes of the East and the West that had waned considerably in the preceding seven years, began to wax again. Journals that had not been obtainable for a long time were once more to be seen. Sending of reprints, and correspondence between individual scholars, increased continuously. In the Soviet Union the vehement, mostly unscientific criticism of Einstein and Bohr ceased, and the first permits for Soviet delegations to attend conferences abroad were issued. It must be stated that often only a few of those invited actually came, but they came despite frequent delays, which were not always to be attributed to bureaucrats in their own country but only too often to the equally reluctant and suspicious authorities in the West.

One of the first nuclear physicists from the West permitted to travel to the Soviet Union in the post-Stalin era was Victor Weisskopf. He had worked in Russian institutes for a time in the

157

thirties, before having to bend to the regime's hostility toward foreigners. In the *Bulletin of the Atomic Scientists* he describes the deep, openly expressed emotion with which his old friends, some of the leading Soviet physicists, embraced him after so many years of separation.

However, more powerful at first than the newly permitted heartfelt expressions of scientific camaraderie, were the obstacles produced on both sides by the cold war. These wrecked an initial attempt to expand CERN to the other side of the iron curtain.

The following hitherto unrevealed episode was described to me by Professor Vasily Emelyanov, long-time director of the Soviet Atomic Energy Agency and later representative of his country to the International Atomic Energy Agency in Vienna: "At the first world 'Atoms for Peace' conference, held in Geneva in September, 1955, I was to send out feelers on behalf of my government regarding the possibility of the socialist countries joining CERN. Of course, all this had to be done very carefully and completely unofficially, for we did not want to meet with a rebuff before the whole world. In fact, when I brought up the subject, it was not taken up with enthusiasm by the West at all. It was pointed out to me, with due decorum and obviously without regret, that the Conseil of CERN had decided not to admit new members until 1959." (I was assured by sources on the Western side that ideological considerations could not have played a part in this polite rejection. CERN had refused to admit Russia as a member state because it wanted to build up in Europe an autonomous research center independent of the two superpowers, USSR and U.S.A. The smaller East European nations were not affected by the veto directed against the superpowers. Yugoslavia had in fact joined CERN, and the other smaller socialist countries were asked to join but had refused when CERN was formed.) "But we did not want to wait so long, *could* not wait so long," Emelyanov continued. "At one of the many receptions given at that time by all the delegations represented in Geneva, I spoke to some prominent Polish and Bulgarian guests about the disappointing results of my efforts. That took place in the middle of Lake Leman; the French minister for atomic affairs at that time, Gaston Palewski, on the inspired advice of his country's General Consul in Geneva, Alexandre de Manziarly, had received us on board one of the charming white steamers that cross Lake Geneva, instead of in a hotel ballroom. Thus, on a sunny autumn afternoon, in the midst of the cocktail party throng, the first plans for our own international laboratory were laid."

Only half a year later, on March 26, 1956, the representatives of ten nations in the socialist camp—Albania, Bulgaria, the People's Republic of China, Czechoslovakia, the German Democratic Republic, the People's Democracy of Korea, Mongolia, Poland, Rumania, and the USSR (joined later by Hungary and Vietnam)—met in the Presidium Building of the Academy of Sciences, on the outskirts of Moscow, to set forth the principles of organization and operation of the Joint Institute for Nuclear Research. The internationally known Russian nuclear physicist Dimitri Ivanovitch Blokhintsev was appointed director, on this occasion, and two eminent scholars (J. M. Danysz, of Poland, and V. J. Votruba, of Czechoslovakia) were to assist him.

While it had taken almost five years (1949–54) for the European laboratory to go from conception to final ratification of the statute (and with the latter, to legal entry into the world), the preparations for the Joint Institute for Nuclear Research could be completed by the participating countries of the Eastern Bloc in a little less than a year. This rapidity is not to be attributed only to the fact that a group of powers with totalitarian structures can make legal and financial decisions without difficulty, but also to the fact that the founding of CERN furnished a valuable pattern for an international project of that type. In addition, research programs in the Eastern undertaking could be started up immediately, rather than at the end of a long period of construction, because the Soviet Union brought to the alliance as a "gift for the newborn" a complete "atomic city," kept secret up to then, and with it a great deal of scientific apparatus, some of outstanding quality, and accommodations for all the people involved.

This new city of about ten thousand inhabitants (nine hundred of them scientists and engineers), situated on the banks of the Volga just before it meets the Moscow-Volga Canal, was called Dubna. It had been built in record time shortly after the end of the war by forced labor and prisoners of war, under the direction of the notorious Lavrenti Beria. The ground, mostly swamp, teeming with snakes, toads, and other mud creatures, was actually not very well suited for supporting large, heavy technical installations. Even today there are rumors that the location had been selected by Beria only because he had a *dacha* in the vicinity and could therefore personally supervise the progress of the construction, in any free time he spent away from Moscow in his country house.

It was an old wives' tale, I was told by Venedekt P. Dzhelepov, one of the leading physicists at Dubna. The terrain near the former fishing village Ivankovo, later renamed Dubna, recommended itself at that time to the planners (Dzhelepov was one of them) through advantages that could be acknowledged objectively: the relative nearness of Moscow, the location on the Volga that would facilitate transportation of the large pieces of apparatus to be shipped from Leningrad, the proximity of a large power plant, and finally, the existence of a forest area that made it possible to camouflage the plant, a precaution still deemed necessary in those years.

In spite of, or perhaps because of, the almost complete sealing off of the territory by special units of the secret police, rumors spread throughout the surrounding area, soon after the start of construction work, that "the bomb" was being manufactured there. In Moscow university circles also, this opinion was widely held. Graduates of the physical-technical institutes of Moscow,

Leningrad, Kharkov, and Kiev were sent to the new atomic city without being informed beforehand about their destination. They received some kind of "travel orders," had to appear at the station on an appointed day, then were transported under surveillance in a northwesterly direction, and finally were set down at an improvised stop in the "middle of the forest," where their future bosses took them in hand. Despite the injunction not to divulge anything about the place or nature of their work, some of these research recruits, on their infrequent leaves to the city, hinted that they had been deemed worthy of working on the "problem" (at that time the code name for the atomic bomb in academic circles).

Also, through other unusual events that were hard to conceal, more and more rumors gradually began to spread about Dubna. Once, a ship that happened to be carrying the giant, many-ton magnets for the planned Big Machine got stuck in the ice not far from Leningrad during an especially hard winter. Normally, a ship would be left to remain in that situation until it was possible for it to continue the voyage, or its cargo would be unloaded and transported over land. But Beria, who had taken it into his head to build up Soviet atomic research in record time, considered that too time-consuming. Therefore, an icebreaker from the Red Fleet was called into action to free this seemingly unpretentious freighter and cut a passage through the ice for it.

After the secrecy surrounding the atomic city had been officially lifted, however, numerous Soviet and foreign visitors were permitted to enter Dubna. From then on the atomic city was not omitted from any of the official tours arranged for prominent visitors. Its status was elevated from "hiding place" to "sight-seeing attraction."

V

The first thing that struck me about the Soviet counterpart of CERN and Brookhaven was the old-fashioned calm that emanated from this spot 110 miles north of Moscow. The broad main streets, lined with pines and fenced front gardens, are reminiscent of those in residential quarters of pre-World War I Berlin. The buildings housing the administrative staffs of the five laboratory groups appear even more old-fashioned. Their façadcs, painted in the characteristic Czarist yellow, and decorated with white columns topped by neoclassical capitals, are imitations of the architecture of the early nineteenth century, the period when the scientific academies at St. Petersburg and Moscow were built. Only buildings started after the opening up of Dubna, such as the Institute for Neutron Physics and some new housing developments, are more functional and contemporary in appearance.

Although Dubna's Big Machine, the 10 BeV synchrophasotron, was the most powerful particle accelerator in the world for over three years (from 1956 to 1959), it is housed in a completely old-fashioned building resembling an oversized concert pavilion in an equally oversized city park of the turn of the century. Though it began operating two years after Stalin's death, in some respects this immense apparatus testifies to the isolation in which Soviet scientists had to live up until 1955. If the "opening up to the West" had been risked somewhat earlier, this accelerator would not have been designed according to outmoded principles, but, like the accelerators of Meyrin and Brookhaven, would have made use of the "alternating gradient system" that makes for very much higher energies.

Thus, in its very first run, the machine was already technically archaic. It contains the largest electromagnets in the world. They were manufactured in the Scientific-Technical Institute for Electrophysical Apparatus in Leningrad, and assembled in Dubna. During the assembling, the Russian "machine physicists," so the story goes, would, as a joke, frighten unsuspecting cleaning women and firemen by suddenly switching on the powerful magnets. The metal water pails were snatched from the women as if by an invisible hand, and the men were dragged by their belt buckles toward the metal blocks, each as high as a house. Apart from that, the physicists got little joy out of their machine. It never developed the intensities hoped for, and did not work satisfactorily from the very beginning.

Although the scientists working in Dubna succeeded in making some important discoveries, their Big Machine functioned so erratically—in contrast to Dzhelepov's excellent synchrocyclotron (with a capacity of 680 million electron volts)—that people still say of it: "First we got gray hair over its many childhood diseases. As soon as they were outgrown, the troubles of old age set in."

Nevertheless, the synchrophasotron was lauded in the socialist countries, in articles, films, and even poems, as a symbol of the technical prowess of the Soviet Union. Its picture still appears in the masthead of the local newspaper, and it is shown to important visitors, who find the external appearance of this Big Machine more impressive than that of the PS in Meyrin, because the instrument is not buried underground, but can be viewed in all its might from a platform inside the large round hall. Scientifically informed visitors are more impressed by the achievements of the four other laboratories that are part of the Joint Institute, however. In particular, the institute in which Professor Florov succeeded in producing several transuranic elements is considered to be a scientific workshop of the highest international caliber.

Niels Bohr's first visit to Dubna was the occasion for a tremendous amount of special preparation by the large family of nuclear physicists, for Bohr and his "Copenhagen school" had been the targets of the most vehement of the attacks by the dogmatists of dialectical materialism during the Stalin period. In the year 1960, however, this staunch advocate of an "open world"—open to the continuous dissemination of new knowledge, open to never-ending criticism, open to discussion across all frontiers—was welcomed in the atomic city as a prophet of greater understanding. A much more pronounced change seemed to be indicated in the relations among scientists than had been anticipated from the first signs of renewed willingness to cooperate.

The particularly open-minded head of the publications division at Dubna, Mikhail Lebedenko, played some tape recordings for me, that had been made during Bohr's visit. On one of them the aged Bohr, in a quivering voice, expressed his hope for a new era of planetary search for truth unhindered by tyranny or censorship. I was also shown all the movies that had been taken at that time. In one, I saw how the gates to the individual laboratories were flung open before the large black limousine bearing the guest. I could not help comparing the atomic city, as it is presented to "very important persons" on official visits, with the Dubna of an ordinary day. For the Joint Institute for Nuclear Research, in contrast to CERN, is a place where the guards at the gate are exact and strict. It is true that they are not posted immediately at the main entrance; they are found instead in front of each of the five separate laboratory complexes. Within the institute as a whole there is no real freedom of movement. Everyone must have a pass permitting him to enter only certain buildings and certain specified sections within those buildings. The premises on which the different research laboratories are located are separated from the outside world by walls, fences, and in part even by cleverly concealed barbed wire. One can enter only through narrow passageways where uniformed guards ask to see the necessary permit.

The guards are never content merely to nod or wave one on. Even laboratory members who have been going by the same guard at least four times a day, for years, are examined as carefully as are newcomers or visitors. The gatekeeper takes the pass, studies it for a painfully long time, then stares into the face of its possessor for a few seconds ("Please remove your sunglasses!"), looks again at the photograph on the pass, and only then hands it back, almost unwillingly.

If someone forgets his papers he must turn back and get them. That can sometimes lead to surprising situations. A Hungarian physicist, refused entry by the guard at the gate, said that when he unexpectedly returned to his apartment he found H., head of the division entrusted with "caring for" non-Russian laboratory members, going through his bookshelves.

When I asked Shvaniev, the functionary in charge of "caring for foreigners" in the laboratory, about this story, he shrugged it off with the remark that it was simply another of the many anti-Soviet rumors that were contantly being invented. There were, in fact, many stories circulating in Dubna that had as their subject the visible and invisible workings of the control agencies. Though their content might have been partly incorrect, the facts upon which they were based were not denied. The stories were an expression of deep dissatisfaction over this kind of control, so inappropriate to a laboratory for basic research. Physicists from Dubna, spending some time in Meyrin, were not surprised by the brimming shop windows in Geneva, nor by the fact that CERN workers owned their own cars. But that "security" was so inconsequential there—that made a deep impression on all of them.

The excuses made by the functionaries for the police measures in Dubna are hardly convincing. One of them tried to tell me, for example, that the main reason for posting guards at the laboratory gates actually was to prevent curious children from entering, and thereby save them from contamination by radioactivity. When I repeated this heart-warming tale at the end of a speech I gave before the Club of Scientists in Dubna, in order to learn the opinion of my audience, my answer was loud, knowing laughter from one hundred throats. The younger generation of scientists is no longer afraid to scoff openly at those methods in which the suspicion of the Czarist and Stalin eras lives on.

VI

If one is willing to accept the supervision and the occasional supply crises in Dubna, life there, in the opinion of many permanent and temporary members of the institute, is very stimulating. As the scientists, unlike those at CERN, are not widely scattered throughout or around a large city, but live near one another, their intellectual and social intercourse is extremely active. In addition, there are a great many cultural events. The member states send theater troupes, orchestras, and films to the atomic city. Also, the leading theater companies of Moscow enjoy performing before this highly intelligent audience, and often conduct artistic experiments there. For example, Bertolt Brecht's plays were performed in Dubna before they could be seen in Moscow. In the House of Culture avant-garde poets regularly read from their works. At the Club of Scientists, editors of leading newspapers appear at open discussions. One of the most exciting of the public debates, occupying people for weeks, and echoing throughout the rest of the country, was conducted in 1963 between nuclear physicists and representatives of the leading journal for Marxist doctrine. Its subject was the relation between dialectical materialism and the latest findings in the natural sciences. In the course of the debate the dogmatism of the party men had to stand up to pointed criticism. "Dubna is a modern city. There is no church here," exclaimed the writer D. Danin, in telling me about these debates. It was fairly obvious that he was not referring only to the Russian Orthodox Church.

The few physicists from the West who remain in Dubna for six months or a year consider the work pace in the institute's laboratories almost relaxing, after the pressures they are accustomed to at home. There is no frantic haste, for in the great race for new discoveries Dubna was left behind several years ago. "In the long run it may not be altogether a disadvantage," I was told by a German nuclear physicist named Walter Fischer, who held one of the six exchange positions at Dubna available to CERN members. "In Dubna physicists still have time to think. Therefore they might possibly find something someday that everybody else has overlooked in his frenzy, and will make a great discovery."

Only in Dubna does the "artificiality" of the atmosphere in the experimental halls of CERN and Brookhaven become obvious. The Russians have not shut nature out of their laboratory, but have deliberately brought it in. In machine shops one can find green plants, flowers, and even tanks of tropical fish. Songbirds flit back and forth in the office of the research group of the young physicist Nikitin (who once visited CERN for half a year). In winter, the birds can fly in and out through closed windows by means of skillfully designed passageways.

True, there is less order here than in Meyrin or Brookhaven. Magazines lie open next to the lathes. Chessboards are scattered between machines. The doors of the bookcases next to the tool chests are always partly open. The "master," an aeronautical engineer who lost a hand in an explosion during World War II, fosters an atmosphere of easygoing relaxation. "Many of my young workers still go to school after work. If they want, I help them with their problems," he told me.

Perhaps the climate of operation in Dubna is more natural because about one third of the employees are women. At CERN women are to be found only in secretarial positions, in the library, and in the Data Handling Division, while in Dubna they are engaged in research and engineering as well. In some divisions women are even group leaders, and the men who work under them claim that they do not mind in the least taking orders from a female boss. ("I'll let you in on a little secret," one scholar told me. "Our girls crowd into science in such numbers today that we have to give them harder problems on exams than we give the young men. That is especially true of medicine. If we didn't take such measures, we'd soon find ourselves in the minority in the laboratories.")

Many of these often very attractive and highly intelligent women scientists are married to other laboratory members. Because of their training they can usually understand what their husbands are talking about when the topic is their work. At CERN, as far as professional matters are concerned, most couples are separated by a non-comprehension gap. When people get together in the evening, very soon the men will be grouped in one corner, talking shop, while the women are left to their own devices.

When I spoke about the matter to Theodore Soprounov, a biology professor at Moscow University, who, as the son of Russian emigrés, had been raised in Paris, he said: "That doesn't surprise me one bit. In the West, you have invisible walls not only between men and women. I go back on visits from time to time. Naturally I envy my colleagues over there for a number of reasons. But even more, I pity them. No—I'm not referring to the standard of living, or politics. I mean the coldness in which almost everyone lives. Everyone is basically alone there. My co-workers and I—we are friends. We belong together. Not only at work. Everyone knows everything about everyone, more or less. At the beginning, when the war brought me back to the country of my birth, this Russian lack of discretion seemed unbearable. Today, I know that it is genuine sympathy, or—if you cynics can still tolerate such a weighty word—love, and I now would no longer want to live the way my former countrymen do."

VII

Most of the physicists who come from the West feel that they cannot afford the slower pace at Dubna, not even for half a year. They look upon these six months that they are out of the "race" for new discoveries as lost time, presumably. Therefore, the positions that CERN could claim in Dubna, according to an agreement concluded in 1960, are almost never filled. The few people who do come, be it out of curiosity, or to give of their knowledge to their Eastern colleagues, are often irritated by the involved bureaucratic methods scientists are subjected to there, and to which they are not accustomed.

Take the case of B., for example. He is a French physicist who had come to Dubna to bring to the construction of a new bubble chamber the experience he had gained in this area in Paris and Meyrin. He waited for weeks for technical material that had been sent to him from CERN. It never arrived. He finally had to conclude that some censoring agency—which, incidentally, did not exist officially—had confiscated the papers for examination. Although B. was known to be a leftist in France, and presumably had no special sympathies for de Gaulle's government, he was forced to turn to his country's embassy for aid in this situation. After a few days he received copies of the "lost" plans—this time, however, they had been sent from Meyrin in the French diplomatic pouch. When during my visit I asked Professor Blokhintsev, then Director of the Joint Institute for Nuclear Research, a man deeply interested in an extensive scientific exchange of information with the rest of the world, whether he could do something to prevent such mishaps, he smiled resignedly, and said: "What do you expect? Anyway, our mail is already a little faster than it was at the time of Genghis Khan."

Some younger members of the institute reacted to the episode much more violently and, as I was to learn, more typically. For, the majority of the scientists in Dubna—and not only the Czechs, Hungarians, Bulgarians, Poles, and Rumanians, but the Russians especially—have for years been pressing with increasing fervor for completely unrestricted cooperation with their colleagues all over the world. They draw upon the fact that the institute's constitution guarantees them freedom of scientific exchange to bring up this subject again and again. Occasionally, there are open disputes with the political authorities.

For example, when a documentary on progress in automatic data-processing of bubble chamber and spark chamber photographs, brought to Dubna by the American physicist Lynn M. Stevenson, was not going to be shown because a functionary thought that the film would only depress the physicists at Dubna, the scientists forced it to be shown. The film revealed how far behind Dubna was, especially in that field. Instead of being depressing, however, it proved to be stimulating.

I have never been anywhere where foreign languages are studied with such alacrity as in Dubna. Instruction in English starts with six-year-olds in the modern school of the atomic city. The classes are taught by a Russian named Bell, who had spent some time in the United States. In the advanced classes, as I witnessed, students speak and read with fluency. There is an English language club for children and adults, which sponsors monthly quizzes and awards prizes to the best linguists.

There is no wonder, then, that most of the scientists at Dubna read British and American technical journals, listen to broadcasts of the BBC in English—with the full knowledge of the institute's leadership, incidentally—and diligently commit to memory an Engish-Russian technical dictionary entitled *Terms and Phrases on Accelerators,* which had been compiled by a charming young lady named Ludmilla Smirnova.

In the sixties Dubna was host to two international physics conferences. On these occasions, things were somewhat more liberal than usual (I was told by the Vice-Director, Heinz Barwich, who later "defected" to the West, that during the conference in 1963 the soldiers of the surveillance units were forbidden to sing in their quarters, so that they would be less conspicuous), and some remnant of this more liberal atmosphere lingered on even after the conferences were over.

Of more lasting effect than these sudden impulses, however, is the influence exerted by the many non-Russian members of the institute. The Poles, Hungarians, Rumanians, and Bulgarians have demonstrated that they could reduce much of the feeling of suspicion in their collaboration with their Russian colleagues. An outward manifestation of this "West-socialist" influence is the Hotel Dubna, built by two Bulgarian architects in a bright, inviting style for an international conference. The architects were given the freedom, as they themselves told me, to apply standards that were not allowed under the Russian building code. When their work met with overwhelming admiration, they were subsequently given permission to erect Western-style apartment houses.

Probably the most important role in this opening-up process was played by a man who, in his native land, Italy, and in his adopted country, England, is looked upon as a defector, even a traitor (although, especially of the latter charge, no evidence has ever been furnished). Bruno Pontecorvo is revered by the young people in Dubna as a symbol of the spiritually independent scientist.

Earlier, in Meyrin, a visiting Soviet physicist had often spoken to me with admiration of Bruno Maximovitch, the first to teach him and others his age in Dubna that serious scientific work is by no means incompatible with humor and a zest for life.

None of the numerous anecdotes about "the excellent skier, water sportsman, and ingenious physicist" (in that order) did I hear in Dubna as frequently as the following:

One day an announcement appears on the bulletin board that Academician Pontecorvo will deliver a lecture on an important new disclosure. The lecture room is overflowing. The presentation, illustrated by numerous slides with curves and figures, makes a deep impression on every listener. When Pontecorvo calls upon the audience for criticism of his bold hypothesis, no one dares utter a word. Then the speaker slaps his forehead and exclaims: "Oh, I forgot to show you the most important slide of all! Where can it be?" An assistant dashes to the lecturer's office and comes back panting. The light is turned off. On the screen, framed by caricatures, appear the words: "April Fool!"

Then the real lecture begins. In it, Pontecorvo demonstrates to his audience, like a magician explaining his tricks, how he had misled them and how they should actually have discovered for themselves the absurdity of it all, through critical analysis that does not yield to the authority of the professor and member of the Academy. "More criticism, comrades, less respect!" were the words with which this April Fool's Day lecture was concluded.

I had the opportunity to speak to Pontecorvo. Despite his more than fifty years, he was as slim and youthful as he had been earlier, when one could still meet him at conferences in the West. I asked him whether the April Fool story was true.

"Yes, that's about the way it was," he said, "but there is something more that you were probably not told: namely, it turned out recently that there was actually something in my joking hypothesis. And now I'm working on the idea in complete seriousness."

VIII

There is a certain irony in the fact that an Italian Communist, denounced by his former countrymen as a renegade, attempts to teach the elite of Soviet youth fundamental attitudes that we consider to be characteristically Western. Occidental thinking broadens into planetary thinking and, in the process, will not for long remain the giver only; more and more it will receive. It seems to me to be remarkable, in this connection, that today it is often the Soviet scientists who transmit to the numerous Asians working in Dubna the originally Occidental concepts of modern natural science, and thus mobilize a huge reserve of new intellectual forces for modern physics.

I will never forget the young theoretical physicist from Vietnam whom I saw for the first time at Professor Blokhintsev's Tuesday seminar. He had asked to speak, had gone to the blackboard, and, speaking rapidly and writing formulae equally rapidly, had expounded his thesis. After a debate that lasted only several minutes, the great "Blokh" had to admit defeat at the hands of the man younger by a generation. It was true, it was the shorter, more elegant solution, thought the head of the laboratory at Dubna, and he was as delighted as his student over the new method. For a second they both stood silent in front of their small audience of about fifty, with similar chalk spots on their hands and jackets. On their faces, at that instant, was written the joy of teaching and the joy of learning.

"He is one of our best people," Blokhintsev told me later. "It is amazing how talented the Asians are, expecially in mathematics and physics. Perhaps it is because they did not have to plow laboriously through to our present position in knowledge from the beginning, but could start from the point where we, laden with tradition, and maybe a bit tired, have managed to arrive. Perhaps, with their freshness and radicalism, they will point out entirely new directions. Today, some of the most original theoretical and experimental physicists are Indians, Chinese, and Japanese. If we had done nothing else in Dubna but help to awaken this slumbering store of scientific talent, our work would have been worthwhile."

Later, I was able to question the twenty-five-year-old Vietnamese about his background. He was the eldest son of a teacher in a village not far from Hanoi. When he was eight years old, his family was compelled to flee the village, destroyed during the war with the French colonialists, and join the guerrilla fighters in the Indo-Chinese jungle.

"Often we had hardly anything to eat," the young man said, "but not a day passed without my father's providing me with some spiritual nourishment. I studied under the open sky in shell holes and underground caverns, often day and night by the light of kerosene lamps. Sometimes with books, but more often without. Learning was the only meaningful thing in these surroundings dominated by meaningless destruction and meaningless death.

"Then came peace with the French in 1954. I was forced, by

the poverty of my family, to do what fire bombs could not bring me to do: to leave off studying and try to earn some money. That was nothing new to me, though. From the time I was twelve I always had to earn my bread somehow, in addition to studying. But this 'in addition' was no longer enough. Twice, I was brought back to school by my teachers. They thought it a waste of talent if I gave up my studies. Finally, the new government awarded me a scholarship. I was to be trained to be a physics teacher at the normal school. An old prof with a white beard, whom the Russians had sent to Hanoi, took me under his wing. Professor Smutny—that was his name—sparked my interest in nuclear physics. That's how I finally got to Dubna."

We sat for many more hours in the small bar at the Hotel Dubna, and the young Asian spoke almost disjointedly about his strongest impressions: the glare of fire over the jungle when General Henri Navarre and his Foreign Legionnaires resorted to a scorched-earth policy; the intellectual insight he experienced for the first time, when he read Louis de Broglie's *Wave Mechanics*; the emotion that filled him when he was reunited with the family he had lost sight of during an air raid and had been separated from for months; the tremendous excitement that had seized him when he felt he had at last understood Heisenberg's work in quantum mechanics. In his hour-long account, the destruction and stimulation that the Occident had brought to Asia, the appreciation and the disdain that it reaps there, were clearer to the listener than ever before.

IX

Less restrained in their criticism of the Western world were the Chinese, while they were members of the Joint Institute for Nuclear Research. They stayed on in Dubna for several years after relations between Moscow and Peking became strained, and it was only in the second half of 1965 that they finally terminated their membership in the Eastern counterpart of CERN.

But before that, they had several times openly displayed their implacable attitude toward non-Communist foreigners. Once, during the visit of an American, and again during the visit of an Indian scientist, the Chinese ostentatiously left their work, to return only after the "imperialist" and the "imperialist's lackey" had departed.

Sixty to eighty strong, the scientists of the People's Republic of China for a long time constituted the second largest contingent in Dubna, after the Soviet Union. They contributed a substantial sum for their membership (one fifth of the total budget), which was sorely missed after their withdrawal.

Even before the open conflict between Moscow and Peking, the Chinese hardly ever mingled with other scientists after working hours. They were almost never seen in the Club of Scientists, hardly ever on the athletic fields or on the popular ski hill that had been a bonus from the excavation for the synchrophasotron.

While most of the non-Russian members of the institute received salaries, adjusted to their home salaries, that were higher than those of the Russian scientists, the Chinese allegedly insisted upon being paid less, and thereby shamed their colleagues. They also did not ask to be assigned individual quarters, in contrast to the other scientists and engineers, and went so far as to insist upon being accommodated as modestly as possible, but communally. They were finally put up in the old Hotel Central on Joliot-Curie Street, which had not been in use since the Hotel Dubna was built. They transformed this rather run-down building into a reservation, entrance to which was strictly forbidden to citizens of other nations.

In the daily participation in the laboratory, relations between the Chinese and the other scientists were marked by propriety, and in some few cases were even friendly. One of the most important discoveries in physics ever made at Dubna, that of a new elementary particle, was announced to the scientific world as the result of cooperation between Soviet citizens and their

Chinese colleagues. (K. C. Wang, who had studied in Germany in the thirties, was even a section head in Dubna for a long time. C. Y. Chao, an equally prominent scientist in Dubna, for a long time maintained contact with his alma mater in Pasadena, California. K. C. Chou, H. Y. Tzu, and Y. Wang corresponded regularly from Dubna with their former countryman, the Nobel Prize winner T. D. Lee, now an American citizen.)

Only after attacks upon Khrushchev's policy of peaceful co-existence had been openly launched by Peking, did the Chinese working in Dubna receive orders from their home country to discuss and to agitate. Then, for several days, the political activists among them attempted to instigate ideological quarrels in the laboratories, in the library, in the Club of Scientists, and even in their private quarters, which were now hospitably open to the comrades—all this while the leadership of the institute looked on. But when the Chinese physicists began to distribute inflammatory material in Russian and in English, the leadership intervened. Among the four Chinese propagandists who were officially expelled from the Soviet Union at that time was the political leader of the Chinese research group in Dubna.

From then on the Chinese remained silent, keeping to themselves even more than they had previously. Everyone expected their government to terminate its membership in the international laboratory and recall its people. But to everyone's surprise, that did not occur. Even the heightening of the crisis between the two great Communist powers did not lead immediately to an end to their collaboration in Dubna. When I asked the Soviet physicist L. I. Lapidus, in February, 1964, how he could account for it, he answered: "We have an optimistic and a pessimistic interpretation. The friendlier version assumes that the traditional solidarity of researchers is more lasting and more important to the Chinese scientists than a temporary ideological dispute. The other explanation is that the Chinese remain in Dubna because, at the moment, it is the only place where their scientific cadre can gain practical experience in the most advanced areas of atomic and nuclear research." (Since the People's Republic of China does not yet have any large accelerators, particle physics is carried out mainly with photographic emulsions exposed to cosmic rays in the observatory on the Lo-hsüeh Mountain, 10,350 feet high, in Yunnan Province.)

"There is concern over the fact that our Chinese colleagues are especially interested in the work done in the Laboratory for Neutron Physics and in the Laboratory for Nuclear Reactions which is—in contrast to the high-energy physics that is done in the other laboratories at Dubna—rather closely related to the construction of atomic reactors and atomic weapons. The idea that this institute, dedicated to the peaceful cooperation of scientists from all parts of the world, might be contributing to the training of designers of Chinese nuclear weapons is, of course, alarming to many of us."

Our conversation was broken off when we entered the large reading room of the Institute for Theoretical Physics, built in 1959, where silence was required, of course. Every seat was taken. On the tables in front of the individual work places, separated from one another by half partitions, there were piles of books and journals from all over the world. While most of the readers looked up and greeted my companion with a nod, a bespectacled Chinese sitting at one of the corner places did not even raise his head. He was completely absorbed in his material. It was not hard for me to recognize, from the cover of the journal he held in his hand, the latest number of a well-known American technical journal.

"If he were completely consistent, he would also have to boycott Western publications," I remarked to my companion when we were outside again.

"Fortunately, he doesn't do that," Lapidus said, "and that gives us some hope. The Chinese physicists often know the work of their Western colleagues far better than we do. They base their own work on it, and try to develop it further. All of us in Dubna believe that in a few years they will be more mature politically. Sometimes they remind us of our own not-so-remote past. The man I liked best to work with, until recently, is a Chinese theoretician. A brilliant mind, full of many entirely original—Oriental, if you prefer—ideas. On questions of revolutionary tactics, however, we could never see eye to eye. But whenever we would get really seriously worked up over political issues, one or the other of us would try to steer the subject back to science, for then we could count on the discussion being reasonable. Why shouldn't we learn to argue rationally about political questions, too? I am convinced that someday social issues will be settled as calmly and as dispassionately as differences of opinion on physics problems."

X

It is customary, unfortunately, to dismiss similar political statements made by scientists as naïve because it is convenient to do so. The negative assessment is based mostly on insufficient understanding of the scientist's way of thinking. When the scientist considers the future, he never makes definite assertions—as is often ascribed to him—but merely puts forth possible hypotheses. Critics would arrive at a fairer judgment of scientists' statements if they were to witness how scientists go about their own work.

Their methods were characterized by the Viennese biologist Wolfgang Wieser in the following way: "There is a tendency to overlook the fact that scientific work does not lead to a catalogue-like description of reality, but to models of reality. The measurable quantities are only the points of intersection of a net, the pattern of which is, for the most part, only conjectured and, to a lesser extent, freely invented. . . . For example, the mechanical model introduced by Descartes three hundred years ago, to explain the functioning of organisms, was an invention that had a decided influence on the development of physiology, and with it the biological sciences. Hardly anything in this model can be accepted as factually correct today; but it anticipated the possibility of conceiving of the living organism as being basically a rational, comprehensible system of interactions of controlling and controlled parts. With this concept began a development that led to the great medical discoveries of modern times."

The scientist is fully aware that his hypotheses will later be confirmed by experiment only in part and only for a limited time. But he also knows that intellectual speculation about the future—which leads to disputes over proof and disproof—has a strong influence on the future, and that without it there is only an accidental, rather than a directed, further development. An example of this is the proposal, discussed for years among high-energy physicists to construct a so-called "world machine," an accelerator through which the planetary cooperation of nuclear scientists would be given as concrete a goal as European cooperation was given, in 1950, by the proton synchrotron project.

Before the end of the century, at a still unspecified spot on the globe, a single technical structure of almost four miles in diameter and twelve and one half miles in circumference would be erected. This monster machine, together with its experimental halls, each 100 yards wide and 600 yards long, would occupy as much space as a sizable city.

This "intercontinental accelerator"—so called in official documents—is no longer merely a physicists' dream, but is already one of the subjects of an international agreement that the United States and the Soviet Union had their respective representatives, John McCone and Vasily Emelyanov, formally sign on November 24, 1959. The agreement provides for cooperation in the future between both powers not only through exchange of personnel and information in the field of the utilization of atomic energy for peaceful purposes, but also through an examination of the feasibility of engaging in joint projects. The agreement specifically refers to "the design and construction of a particle accelerator of a large and novel type."

In August and September of 1960, informal discussions about

the "super-energy accelerator" took place between American and Soviet physicists in Rochester, New York, and in New York City. Both sides agreed at that time that the new apparatus would have to produce energies ten to thirty times higher—or even more—than those of the Brookhaven and Meyrin proton synchrotrons. Energies of 400, 700, and even 1,000 BeV were considered desirable goals for the "intercontinental machine."

The two groups from the East and the West were to meet again a year later, in September, 1961, in Brookhaven, for a comparison of conclusions. But the Soviet representatives did not appear at the scheduled meeting, and offered no explanation for their change of heart. When I asked Professor Veksler for the possible reasons for their absence, he thought that a "jump" from an energy of about 30 BeV to one so many times larger had seemed to him, and most probably to the majority of Soviet physicists also, after a more detailed examination, simply to be too great. Even Emelyanov, who had actually brought the agreement about, drew back. In a conversation I had with him in Dubna, he said that there were more urgent international projects to be tackled first by the great powers in cooperation, such as the construction of continental and even intercontinental power grids that could be fed by large jointly operated atomic power plants. Peace in the world would be more firmly grounded through the material ties of technology, he thought. A third Soviet physicist from Dubna (who asked me not to reveal his name) was of the opinion that his government did not have sufficient means to engage simultaneously in a costly armaments program and in the extension of its space program, and then, on top of that, to construct such a huge machine. The superaccelerator was the easiest project to abandon.

Doubts about the feasibility of the project for the moment, for political reasons, were also voiced by the Americans. Wolfgang Panofsky, the Director of the Stanford Linear Accelerator, who is extremely familiar with conditions in the Soviet Union, said that if the large and complicated machine was to be built in partnership, one-day visits and verbal communications were not enough. The designers would have to have free access to all the research plants of the partner country and would actually have to live there. But the Soviet research institutions were not so open at the time. During a conversation I had with Professor Rabi, he raised the question of whether a joint East-West large-scale technical project today would really be in the interests of peace. It might, under certain circumstances, produce more tensions than it would alleviate.

"What would happen, for instance, if our engineers rejected a part supplied by the Russians for not meeting specifications?" he asked. "Just imagine how much ill-feeling that would generate. Only when people know one another well enough not to take criticism as insult but as assistance can such joint international undertakings be productive. The Europeans had finally become ready for that after the Second World War. The Russians and Americans are not ready yet, unfortunately."

It was not surprising, therefore, that a summit conference of leading American, European, and Russian physicists held in Vienna in July, 1964, and sponsored by the Union of Pure and Applied Physics in order to activate the plan for the "world machine," ended without any practical results. "The Russian participants did not seem to be willing to come to terms on the respective scientific, technological, and organizational questions," reported a Western delegate who took part in this last attempt to put the agreement of 1959 into action. This temporary setback did not mean the complete termination of the "super-energy accelerator" project. The Americans as well as the Russians continued to make plans for a giant machine. The United States team, which had started on design studies as early as 1960 and 1961, and looked into the experimental program requirements for a 300 to 1,000 BeV accelerator, even published their findings. The public was first informed in this way about the huge dimensions of this technical creation that might very well be the most stupendous ever planned.

The distances between individual parts of this machine were so great, one learned from the design study edited by L. C. L. Yuan and J. P. Blewett, that the "conventional methods of data and command signal transmission may not be economically feasible for these large machines." One would no longer rely upon cable connections, but would have to consider the latest techniques of telemetering (those used between spaceships and ground stations, for example). Also, the quantities of information and the number of command signal controls required for such a monster are so much greater that they are impractical for human management. Therefore electronic scanning would have to be employed. Some of the experimental beams coming from the machine would extend over distances of the better part of a mile or more. Since the "trillion machine" could be expected to produce much more intense radioactivity than do the largest accelerators in existence today, the vacuum chamber where the protons would circulate would have to be buried under about thirty feet of earth. Repairs and other operations could be performed only by remote control from shelters shielded by lead and concrete from the dangerous radiation remaining after runs.

The Soviet Union also did not discontinue planning for its Big Machine. But very little is known of the details of their design. First one learned only that Valentin Petukhov and Alexander Mintz had reported to the Academy of Sciences on their work in connection with the super-energy accelerator. Then, at the international accelerator conference held in Dubna in August, 1963, two large-scale projects were put forth for consideration by the Soviet physicists: a 500 BeV machine that had been designed in Moscow at the Institute for Theoretical and Experimental Physics, and a completely new, 1,000 BeV machine, based on cybernetic principles. The latter project would first be tested on a 1 BeV model, in the new city of scientists, Akademgorodok, near Novosibirsk.

Despite the separate plans, the physicists have not given up hope of an eventual united project. Dr. G. Kenneth Green, Chairman of Brookhaven's Accelerator Department, declared in March, 1965, before a United States congressional committee on atomic energy:

"We maintain continuous contact with design groups across the United States, in Western Europe, and in the Soviet Union. This contact is maintained by visits, by telephone, by exchange of people for periods of months, by exchange of reports, and by correspondence. Our final design report will include ideas from many laboratories and will be based on the worldwide cooperation of the fraternity of accelerator builders and high-energy physicists."

Thus, there already exist today some of the "higher forms of combat" that the Austrian historian Friedrich Heer wished for. They are fought with weapons that require no less ingenuity, but sow no death and destruction. And so, together with seeds of war, seeds of peace are to be found, the existence of which is only too little known. The idea of international research centers is broadening, however: more and more worldwide research projects, research years, and research decades are being proposed and are even being partly realized.

Is there at last a new force that is more effective against the unsolved spiritual and material conflicts threatening our future than the old-style "peace movements" ever were?

Without manifestos, without proclamations, and without demonstrations, the planetarians in the laboratories of almost every country more and more have adjusted their thinking and working to one another. This side effect of their work—nowadays possibly more urgent than new findings in the natural sciences—could be the salvation of an earth threatened by destruction.

SEVEN

The
Meaning

I

When I set out for my final visit to CERN, I got caught in a traffic jam near the church of Meyrin. The long line of barely moving cars, trucks, oil trucks, and construction machines shimmering in the vapor from the exhausts extended far down to the French border. It was not the police who held us up, nor the occasional flock of sheep somewhat unfamiliar with traffic regulations, but an enormous crane on wheels, which had gone over the shoulder of the road.

"Since they began building again at CERN, this sort of thing happens all the time," grumbled one of the waiting drivers. The area around the laboratory had undergone a complete change since my last visit, through new construction. Across the slightly sloping green fields on the right stretched new high-tension lines, and the new connecting road to France seemed finally to be finished.

In the lab, commotion, unrest, noise, and the mood of impatient expectancy were more pronounced this time than on my earlier visits. CERN was breaking out of its bounds. It was reaching across the border. The green meadows on the other side of the frontier were dotted with men and machines. The signs proclaiming the beginning of the territory of the Republique Française were of as little concern as the gray stone markers inscribed with the fleur-de-lis, remnant of the Bourbon era.

Ninety-five acres of French soil had been leased for the nominal sum of about $2.50 annually and added to the Swiss grounds of the research center. There, excavations were already under way for the storage rings, the two giant offshoots of the Big Machine, which were to be fed trillions of protons every few seconds from their "mother," through a long forked duct. "The two rings are concentric," explained the man from the information service. "They intersect at eight positions. At these points the accelerated protons will not hit a fixed target, as is usually the case, but will collide with other particles traveling at the same high speed. Head-on collision with much higher kinetic impact! With colliding beams, almost all the kinetic energy can go into the creation of new particles, whereas with stationary targets most of the energy goes into recoil of the particles. From this point of view the storage rings are equivalent to a conventional accelerator of 1,700 BeV. It would be better to say 1.7 TeV, a unit already becoming popular, for we will soon cross the border between the BeV world and the TeV (trillion electron volt) world."

At the moment, I was more interested in the political ramifications of this new phase of CERN's development than in these physicists' dreams of the future. From previous conversations with Madame Claude Tixier, wife of the well-known French politician, who had conducted negotiations on behalf of CERN with the authorities of both countries, I knew how many novel problems in civil and international law the expansion of the laboratory had presented for lawyers and administrators. "A few good doctoral theses on international law will come out of it," were the words with which this delicate, energetic woman would console herself when the jungle of legal paragraphs seemed impenetrable. Then some progress would be made, and new problems would emerge. How could one manage to have an opening in the border without having guards posted directly in front of the Swiss and French entrances to the laboratory (a situation CERN's directors would never permit)? Which labor and social legislation would apply in the "land of CERN" ? Under whose jurisdiction would it be, and under which police? Those of the canton of Geneva, as before, or those of the Pays de Gex as well? Would telephone calls from the French part of the laboratory to Geneva be billed as foreign calls? Nonsense. But might that not be considered a pretext for a silent "annexation" of French territory? And what would happen if a crisis, perhaps even a revolution, were to break out in one of the two countries in which CERN is situated? Could half of the lab be occupied by a national guard as a security measure, while the other half remained without armed protection?

Twice, formal signing of an agreement had been scheduled and then postponed. Once, champagne for the toasts following the ceremony had even been purchased and then (allegedly) sent back. Finally, the time had come: on September 25, 1965, almost exactly eleven years after its founding, CERN became an international research center territorially also.

II

I had expected that this expansion, and the proposed construction of an important large-scale scientific-technological device of a new type, would arouse as much enthusiasm in CERN's scientists as had the construction of the Big Machine in the fifties.

But I came upon many doubts. Would the laboratory, which was already much too big, completely lose its special character? Would the "spirit of CERN" be driven out and replaced by the anonymity of a soulless research plant? I heard debates in the cafeteria over what the maximum number of employees in a research institution should be. One thousand? Fifteen hundred (as Pierre Auger had once claimed)? Two thousand? Someone quoted from a talk by Wolfgang Panofsky, the witty, well-known American physicist, who had just finished constructing the world's largest electron accelerator in California, the "monster" of Stanford. According to his observations, two thirds of the private conversations in Big Science institutes centered on administrative problems, one tenth was devoted to gossip, and at most one quarter to the scientific work itself. CERN, too, was in the process of preparing another administrative reform. The twelve existing "divisions" were to be transformed into seven "departments." I remembered a remark Gentner had made, partly in jest, a short while before in Heidelberg, when we were speaking about the future development of CERN. He had said: "The engineers will take over." And I had added to myself: "Together with the administrators."

The enthusiasm I had expected I found only in two divisions. One was that of Charles Peyrou, perhaps the most popular head of an *équipe* in CERN, an unusually alert, witty southern Frenchman, who hides his phenomenal efficiency behind an easygoing façade, and knows how to combine demands for disciplined work with genuine camaraderie. He had succeeded in getting the eighty-inch bubble chamber to work, after several years of exacting labor. He and others were now tinkering with larger "toys": a *chambre de bulles* that they had named *Gargamelle* after Rabelais's glutton is being built by the French for use at CERN; a giant twelve-feet-long liquid hydrogen bubble chamber is also under construction as a collaborative effort of France, Germany, and CERN itself, as even bubble chambers have become too expensive to be financed by a single country. I also found enthusiasm in Kjell Johnsen's group. The Norwegian had, years ago, assisted Odd Dahl in designing the PS. In the fifteen years that had elapsed since then, he had gained the reputation of being one of the world's ten leading accelerator specialists. Yet he still looked like a student. His youthfulness remained with him even in the position of great responsibility, supervisor of construction of the storage rings—a project that was to cost three times as much as the Big Machine!

When I saw, in Johnsen's office, the volumes of calculations, blueprints, and time schedules on the shelves, I realized how much more preparation had gone into this new project than into the PS. It had profited from the surprises and setbacks of the earlier project, and this time much more detailed and inclusive plans had been worked out. No less than the physical and technical skills had the ability of Kjell Johnsen's generation to prognosticate also grown. The newly created "science of decision making" (which employs flexible cybernetic methods and complex computer programs to show the various profiles of the future) enabled them to develop an astonishingly precise strategy for making the best possible use of men, material, and financial means. To dream of the future was not enough. The future must be calculated. Fantasy and calculation were no longer incompatible but simply two phases of the same process, belonging together and depending upon one another in the same manner as do theory and experiment, appearance and reality. And yet I could understand why the Swiss physicist Paul Preiswerk, one of the founders of CERN, had waxed a bit nostalgic over the days when the PS had been in a stage similar to the present one of the storage rings: "Naturally this time everything is being planned much more thoroughly. We know where we're going. But some of the feeling of adventure that drove us then has been lost. And it probably can never be retrieved."

CERN's storage rings, to be completed by the beginning of the seventies, are only one aspect of a more comprehensive plan for the further development of European nuclear physics, worked out by a commission established in January, 1963, and headed by Edoardo Amaldi. The main feature of the plan is the construction of a continental proton synchrotron,* which, though not as large as the projected "intercontinental machine," nevertheless, with an energy of 300 BeV, would be ten times as energetic as the PS of Meyrin. This super-energy accelerator can be likened to the apex of a pyramid. It would be built on a base of smaller and medium-sized accelerators, which would be constructed by the individual member states of CERN. In addition, one of the future projects is the continuous improvement of the good old PS and its experimental halls. This balanced European research program would require of all nations participating in CERN a substantial increase over previous expenditures for high-energy physics. The plan calls for an expenditure in 1977 of 1.6 billion Swiss francs (approximately $400 million), which is less costly, however, than the American program, in which, for the same year, federal support for high-energy physics is anticipated to be $600 million.

These are enormous sums, and it is not at all certain that the CERN member states will ratify the proposal in its entirety. If they should ratify the entire plan, then the new Big Machine (the site for which had not been selected by the beginning of 1968, despite much discussion in the Council) would become the heart of a network of physics institutes and research plants spread over Europe. The various institutes would be as closely connected as if they were a single large lab. For instance, the data-processing machines of all the institutions would be coupled to three projected central computers, and would work with them "on line." Furthermore, facilities for traveling back and forth, at any time, between the different divisions of this institu-

---

* The following data on this new European accelerator are known: circumference: 4.7 miles; diameter: 1.5 miles; number of magnets: 864; total weight of magnets: 31,000 tons; number of vacuum pumps: 664; number of employees at the end of construction: 4,500; size of terrain: at least eight square miles; construction time: seven to eight years; costs (according to 1964 levels): about $370 million.

tion distributed over ten to twelve different countries, would be available to the institute members in the form of an internal airline.

III

It will cost a billion dollars,
Ten billion volts 'twill give,
It will take five thousand scholars,
Seven years to make it live.

. . .

This machine is just a model
For a bigger one, of course.
That's the future course of physics
As I am sure you'll all endorse.

. . .

Take away your billion dollars,
Take away your tainted gold,
Take, oh, take your billion dollars,
Let's be physicists again!

These stanzas from a song by the American physicist Arthur Roberts, composed immediately after the end of World War II and before the construction of Brookhaven's cosmotron, proved to have been a remarkably accurate prophecy. The discomfort expressed in them was revived in the middle sixties when the plans for the construction of still larger machines became known. It stemmed, as I learned, from various sources.

The high numbers, so impressive to the layman, aroused in most of the physicists involved in designing the 300 BeV machine not a feeling of enthusiasm but rather one of inadequacy. For them, this project represented, in essence, nothing better than a simple scale-up of the well-proven "atom smashers" of Meyrin and Brookhaven. It was not a symbol of progress but the admission of a technical standstill.

A similar situation had prevailed before, in 1951, when CERN first decided to build an accelerator that would have been essentially a greatly enlarged version of an older accelerator. At that time, Livingston, Ernest Courant, and their associates had found their solution in the "alternating gradient synchrotron," a solution that was not only more elegant but more economical and more powerful as well. This time the physicists had hoped in vain for the appearance of an equally radical idea. One of their hopes had not been fulfilled, that of obtaining smaller and more powerful magnets by the use of superconductivity (which had been demonstrated experimentally in several laboratories). These developments were simply not in a sufficiently advanced stage to be applied to a high-precision research tool. Other seemingly interesting proposals, such as those put forward by the two Soviet physicists Vladimir I. Veksler and Gershon Budker, had not withstood the test of more detailed examination. Thus one was forced to take up this "clumsy giant thing," with the uncomfortable feeling that in a few years, when it would be too late to turn back, the hoped-for revolutionary solution might be found. But the long breaking-in period required by such enormous projects demanded that preparations be started early, and that the design be "frozen," as the technical term goes, even though it might not be the best one possible.

Far more basic than these technical considerations are other doubts with which the nuclear physicists struggle, in their search for the meaning of their work.

In the first, at times painful phase of their struggle for self-understanding, which began in Los Alamos and Chicago during the war, physicists had been confronted with the possibility that their work might alter the world beyond recognition. Now they were meeting the reproach that their current work altered the world too little, that their research had become too far removed from reality to warrant such enormous sums. Was Alvin M. Weinberg, Director of Oak Ridge National Laboratory, correct in his assertion that the contributions of high-energy physics to other branches of science, to technology, or even to mankind in general did not justify the huge amounts spent or the haste in which they were being spent? Was Philip Abelson, editor of the American journal *Science*, right when, in a comparison of molecular biology, unmanned space exploration, and high-energy physics, he gave the last the lowest rating in terms of social merit? Did the following words of the Soviet physicist Lev Andreevich Artsimovitch apply to the scientists at CERN? "Scientific research is a means by which private curiosity is satisfied at public expense."

Professor Cocconi, one of the most capable and deepest thinkers at CERN, asked himself and his colleagues, in 1964, when construction of the storage rings was being deliberated, "Could it not be that we are a caste of maniacs, who try to solve the problems created only by our machines, problems not all-important for the equilibrium of nature, the nature we live in?" For himself, Cocconi had answered the question in the negative. Not long ago, in Meyrin, to while away the time, he and his friend Philip Morrison had thought up the first primitive "language" for communication between man and creatures on distant stars. Now he raised his eyes heavenward and found there the answer to the meaning of his work. In the universe, he explained, there are regions where, according to the findings of the radio astronomers, matter is presumably composed of particles like those produced on earth in the Big Machines. There, space had the dimensions of light-years, and was filled with millions of suns. "Perhaps all galaxies, all of us, went or will go through that stage. Thus the BeV, the TeV world cannot be an abstraction, since it is deeply connected with the nature that surrounds us. It is even imaginable that we might some day use it to advantage."

But by no means all physicists can find their work justified with a glance toward the stars. The want in their earthly surroundings—plagued by hunger and war, and threatened by even greater catastrophe unless constructive plans are soon prepared with as much foresight and exactness as are devoted to the construction of Big Machines—raises doubts about whether their luxury science can still be justified.

The new grandiose plans of the leading people are sometimes treated with humor by their colleagues; this became clear to me when I read a copy of an article from *Orbit*, the journal put out by the Rutherford High Energy Laboratory (the smaller, British counterpart of CERN) that was making the rounds in the cafeteria at Meyrin. Under a heading that had a somewhat familiar ring to everyone there, "The Future of the European Harmonic Pendulum Program," the article stated that it had become absolutely necessary to construct a giant harmonic high-energy pendulum for the furthering of European culture. Since the instrument was to be 1,400 feet long, it would be best to suspend it from the Eiffel Tower, for the investigation of "a new theory on the nature of art and artistic expression."

It went on to give specific details. "Since the tower is only 985 feet high, a hole 415 feet deep would have to be dug at its base, but this device would put European artists in a position to compete with the Americans on almost equal terms. The United States Congress has recently approved a project for a 1,720-foot machine that was to be suspended from the Empire State Building. . . ." It continued in this way for several pages, and was illustrated with sketches of the "Trianglotron," "Berserkatron," and "Light Hysterion." I, too, had the feeling that I had read something like that before. It was, as I was finally to learn, the study made by CERN for the future European accelerator program. Individual sections had been quoted almost verbatim, except that the terms "high-energy physics" and "high-energy accelerator" had been replaced by "art" and "high-energy pendulum."

IV

American scientists have given the most searching and systematic consideration to the problem of the significance of the large laboratories, the Big Machines, and the great expenditures for basic research. In the United States, too, disputes focused on nuclear research as an especially costly branch of science, quite unfamiliar to the public, and which for the time being had no practical applications. The disputes began in 1961 with the now famous article in which Alvin M. Weinberg coined the term Big Science, and decried the partly corrupting influence on American universities of this type of science, which had evolved since the end of the war. Later, in April, 1963, upon publication of a study prepared at the request of President Kennedy on the future perspectives of high-energy physics, the chorus of criticism rose. (For the seventies alone, $400 million in federal support was suggested, a sum high even by American standards.) The nuclear physicists were forced by the objections to show the relevance of their research to other sciences and to society. In doing so, they demonstrated a high degree of self-criticism and maturity.

The entire debate, conducted with admirable fairness and objectivity on the part of each participant, merits being made known outside the small circle of people immediately concerned. The main issue under discussion was: "What benefit does society derive from research?" Such questions of "research strategy" should interest the public today at least as much as the great discussions on foreign and military policy did earlier, for the conquests of science affect the lives of all citizens no less than did the conquests of armies and navies in the past.

It is remarkable that the debate on the future of nuclear physics in the United States found its highest expression, not in an academic discussion, but in a congressional hearing. On the first four weekdays in March, 1965, a hall in the Capitol in Washington was turned into a seminar room. With the aid of slides, graphs, tables, and models, in individual statements, dialogues, and panel and round-table discussions, thirty-four of the leading American scientists and the nine members of the

Senate and House of Representatives who constituted the Sub-committee on Research, Development and Radiation of the Joint Committee on Atomic Energy argued the content, significance, and prospects of modern physics.

These hearings represented, on a higher level and in a more advanced stage, the same kind of novel and meaningful democratic self-scrutiny as did the discussions, in 1953, on the referendum of the Genevans as to whether CERN could be established in their canton. When I read through the eight-hundred-page green volume containing the proceedings, I was as astounded by the amount of scientific knowledge the American congressmen had acquired as I was by the clarity with which most of the scientists testifying before the representatives of the people expressed the most difficult subjects in their special fields.

Through three kinds of arguments, the partisans of high-energy physics tried to convince the members of Congress that the United States should continue to give full support to nuclear physics research. First, it was necessary to maintain the position of leadership American nuclear physics enjoyed at the moment. Second, several times before, ideas and experiments that showed no initial promise of practical applications had later effected the technical revolutions that characterize our time. Similarly, the present seemingly enormous expenditures for basic research in nuclear science would presumably "pay dividends" at a later date, although at the moment one could not say how or when. Third, the most advanced fields of research have always transmitted profound, albeit hard to measure, cultural and educational efforts to the general intellectual tone of society. A halt in the field of physics might result in a general stagnation of civilization. Surprisingly enough, this last argument carried more weight than the not quite convincing attempts of the notoriously internationally minded physicists to appeal to national pride, or to laud the winged horse of pure science as the draft horse of technology.

V

Seldom have outsiders learned in such an impressive way, and in such detail, from the pioneers at the frontier what things are like "out there," as during the Washington hearings. They learned about the experiences vouchsafed the seeker of a truer, deeper representation of nature, and how, beyond considerations of national glory and economic advantage, man is striving toward his higher, his true, destiny.

On the first morning, in a masterly fashion, thirty-five-year-old Professor Murray Gell-Mann of California Institute of Technology in Pasadena introduced the congressmen to the symmetric systems propounded by him and other theoretical physicists, in which the growing number of newly discovered particles are grouped into families of eight or ten. The scheme, which has been compared to Dmitri I. Mendeleev's periodic system of the elements, had received sensational experimental confirmation in February, 1964. The omega-minus particle, that had been predicted in all its characteristics by Gell-Mann on the basis of his scheme, had been found, by means of the accelerator and detectors at Brookhaven. This experiment made it seem likely that nuclear physics would be able to bring order to the concepts that had been confused by the latest discoveries. And it was possible that the fundamental constituent of matter postulated by Gell-Mann, the so-called "quark," would play an important role.

Room AE-1 of the Capitol had already been witness to negotiations over duties on watches, consular treaties, subversive activities, and unrest in Southeast Asia. Now, highly unusual talks on revolution and chaos in the world of the smallest dimensions were taking place within its walls.

Dr. Gell-Mann (in his statements on strongly interacting particles): "It may be, in fact, that they are all made up of one another, in a wonderful manifestation of self-consistency."

Representative Hosmer: "Is that the so-called bootstrap [theory]?"

Dr. Gell-Mann: "Bootstrap, precisely. These particles pull themselves up by their own bootstraps in constituting one another in a self-consistent fashion. The older view is that among these strongly interacting particles there must be some small number of fundamental constituents. That may be true indeed; we don't know. What is clear now—and this is really fairly revolutionary, if you think about it, although it has come on us rather gradually—what is clear is that the neutron and proton, regarded for a long time as the basic constituents of nuclear matter, are not in any sense fundamental. If anything is fundamental, it is probably a set of three extremely peculiar particles that no one has ever seen, called 'quarks'. . . ."

Dr. Val Fitch (professor of physics, Princeton University): ". . . the details of the basic force between the proton and neutron are not clear. The proposal of Yukawa in 1935 that the strong nuclear forces be explained on the basis of the exchange of a meson, coupled with the discovery of the pi-meson in 1947, would seem to go a long way toward an understanding —and we believed this well into the 1950's. However—as Professor Gell-Mann has said—we now have to contend with many mesons. And we know now that the neutron and proton are themselves only members of a much larger class of particles and hardly unique. . . . But the high degree of ordering which has appeared among these particles—the symmetries which are present—suggest, still, the possibility of relatively simple answers. For example, the suggestion that all of the strongly interacting particles are composed of three fundamental entities— the quarks—is extremely attractive, and I think you should have Professor Gell-Mann tell you why he labeled these particles 'quarks.' "

Chairman Holifield: "Dr. Gell-Mann, will you . . . give us the origin of the term 'quark'?"

Dr. Gell-Mann: ". . . *Finnegans Wake* by James Joyce is

usually interpreted as being about a bartender's dream. Humphrey Chimpden Earwicker is the bartender. Occasionally in the book he seems to come to the surface. This usually coincides with the striking of the clock. . . . At one point he sort of comes near the surface and mumbles to himself, 'Three quarks for Master Hark. . . .' My personal guess is that the quark is made up of 'quart' and 'hark.' Hark, because he is being awakened by the clock and quart because when he hears a number like three in his profession it usually comes with a word like 'quarts' following. So, from three quarts and hark, perhaps he makes up three quarks. Three quarks—if there is anything at the root of the strong interaction, it would be three quarks."

.　　.　　.　　.　　.

Chairman Holifield: "I think with the three 'quarks' we have just had, as designated by the sound of the buzzer and the sight of the three lights, we are obliged to answer a quorum call at this time. We will resume at two o'clock. . . ."

VI

If quarks really exist, they will be produced only by accelerators with energies a good deal higher than those of the largest present-day machines, the physicists emphasized at the hearings in Washington. Dr. Luke Yuan of Brookhaven National Laboratory held that quarks would perhaps be found at an energy of about 210 BeV. Also, both for a more precise study of "weak interactions" and for the discovery of the "intermediate boson" that Faissner and others had hoped but failed to find in the neutrino experiments, a proton machine of higher energy, of the order of several hundred BeV would be required. With the failure for the time being of the efforts to construct a "world machine," there are now four super-energy accelerator projects in various stages: the 70 BeV machine of the Russians in Serpukhov, completed in November of 1967; a 200 to 500 BeV machine which will be constructed near Weston, Illinois, near Chicago; the "storage rings" of Meyrin; and the 300 BeV European accelerator, construction of which will almost certainly not be completed before 1975.

The debate over whether it is beneficial, or even meaningful, for governments to finance such tremendous projects will go on, and will involve more and more people. Some of them might then ask themselves the two questions the Republican Representative from California, Craig Hosmer, addressed to Professor Fitch at the Washington hearings, in a disarmingly simple manner: "About this work you are doing, can you give us a little hint as to what it may be leading toward?" and: "What does that mean to the average American? This is a fellow who is putting up the money for this. . . ."

The professor replied first with a brief description of the famous experiment in which he and his team shook the foundations of the physical symmetry rules by furnishing evidence for a "violation of CP invariance"; then he continued:

"Essentially I should ask, what does it mean to my wife? I have to answer this in the following terms. We don't know at the present stage just where this idea will lead us. Maybe it will overthrow completely our notion of how the world operates, what makes the world tick. Maybe we will have to modify all the basic equations. If you ask whether this will make it easier for people to have bread and butter around the world, I don't know. But the point is that one is increasing his understanding of the universe, and in the past this has always led, so far as I know, to great benefits."

VII

Decisions are not made in congressional hearings. Preparations for objective decisions are made there, however, through the gathering of extensive, firmly grounded information. In this sense, apart from a slowing down of the increase in support for high-energy physics, the Washington hearings of March, 1965, had no immediate dramatic consequences. It had come out in the course of the discussions that no one present had contemplated cutting off support for high-energy physics. However, two of the participants, Philip Abelson and Professor Eugene Wigner, had advocated moving high-energy-physics research lower down on the list of priorities, in favor of other, more urgent research problems (molecular biology, materials science, psychology). Their arguments did not fail to leave an impression. This basic discussion was by no means concluded with that. The issues will time and again bring about a confrontation between the supporters of the argument—which is more immediately obvious—that science should have direct social benefit, and those who hold that the best way to obtain the practical is not to pursue it.

The latter attitude was expressed beautifully by the British Nobel Laureate Cecil F. Powell in the following words:

"Man does not live by bread alone, and the benefits derived from science are not to be measured only in terms of its technological consequences. Our forefathers made great decisive contributions to all the arts; to music and drama; to sculpture and architecture; to painting and literature; they built the Parthenon and the Cathedrals of Chartres and Bourges, Durham and Salisbury, Toledo and Burgos, Pisa and Lucca, Freiburg and Ulm. All these things gave little economic return but who would regret the effort? In our time, it is in the sciences that the human creative spirit finds one of its chief means of expression. We must therefore encourage the most gifted of our youth to apply themselves to the most difficult, significant, and demanding of the sciences, and at the present time that must include the physics of elementary particles."

In statements like these—seldom made these days, because very few scientists would risk defending their work as the pure search for truth—a turn is indicated, which could be of great significance for the future mentality of a scientized world.

In the last century, research in the natural sciences had more and more become the victim of its own success. The original purpose of research was to free man from superstition and tyranny. In learning how to control nature, and in disclosing it as a source of new wealth and power, the concepts and instruments for an increasingly effective control of people by people have been furnished at the same time, according to the philosopher Herbert Marcuse of the University of California.

At present, the study of subnuclear reality has brought about huge industrial complexes giving rise to phenomena whose meaning cannot yet (nor will for quite some time) add to our further control of natural forces, except that we may contemplate it and elucidate it. Nor does it offer new possibilities for exploitation except for deepening our knowledge.

There is probably some profound significance in the fact that these counterbalances to pragmatic thinking, to the obsession for output and profit, to the mania of getting something out of everything and everybody, resemble outwardly the strongholds of production, the workshops and factories; yet their thousands of mechanics, engineers, clerks, and scientists devote themselves in the final analysis to something intangible, something spiritual. It presages (perhaps prematurely) a time when the manufacture of necessities may no longer be at the core of human effort, because improved means of production and greater organizational skills will have rendered the satisfaction of material wants a concern of secondary importance.

VIII

Seen in this light, the meaning of Gilberto Bernardini's words to his fellow countryman Alberto Cavallari, visiting him at CERN, becomes clear. "Our role is similar to that of the Tuscan monks who, in their time, in the seclusion of their monasteries, opposed the disorder and violence around them. . . ."

Bernardini also recognizes the danger in this role, however.

"Isn't it possible," he mused during a conversation with me, "that we physicists, sequestered in our laboratories, are becoming more and more like a caste of learned priests who, instead of setting a shining example to the world, are only concerned with their own more and more specialized worries and problems? Might this withdrawal tendency not become even more exaggerated if folly and ugliness in the world around us increase?"

Michael Pentz, an outstanding British physicist, who has been at CERN for years, thought that we have already reached that point. The political and social interests of his colleagues were not increasing, but were diminishing steadily. They preferred not to be bothered by "all the nonsense" going on outside. I was struck by the alarming thought that the attractions of this *univers des chercheurs*—bright counterpart to the sinister *univers concentrationnaire,* so masterfully described by Daniel Rousset and Eugen Kogon—might perhaps have so great a hold on many of the creative minds of our time that they will be lost to a society that needs their acuteness and altertness more than ever.

But are not such deliberations again characterized by pragmatic thinking, asking for all too immediate impact in too short a period of time? Is it not conceivable that these *hauts lieux* of modern thinking, these "higher places," as the physicist Louis Leprince-Ringuet would like to view modern large-scale laboratories, will have a strong influence on the mentality and the history of their time, even though they have no direct interaction with the events of the day? Do the men and women working there penetrate deeper, to where the roots of misery lie?

Something else can be said against the thesis of the detached egoism of scientists. That is that most scientists withdraw from social reality only for a limited span in their lives. Many attempt, through speaking, writing, and above all through advising, to influence the direction of events. But if some of them, under the guise of reason, carry out the affairs of unreason by designing new weapons and new military strategies, they come up against the many who, without fanfare, try to see to it that, in the places where power is wielded, the right of criticism, the objective consideration of facts, and the search for ever new solutions, are upheld. Their history still remains to be written. Within today's leadership, composed of politicians, industrialists, military men, and scientific advisers, there is constant struggle, each faction attempting to use the others for its own purposes. Although the scientists, who have become the indispensable intellectuals in a "scientized world," are the weaker materially, they are however steadily gaining ground, because a world that has evolved out of their thinking cannot in the long run be successfully governed other than by a political thinking to match.

In an open letter that Victor Weisskopf wrote to Alvin Weinberg, from the vantage point of CERN, in answer to Weinberg's criticism of high-energy physics, there is a sentence that must have sounded shockingly optimistic to many, only one year after it was written: "Basic research . . . creates the intellectual climate in which our modern civilization thrives." Regular reading of the newspapers makes one inclined to add cynically: "— and is destroyed." But perhaps that is only superficially true of our century. On a deeper level the "optimistic hypothesis" might ultimately prove to be the correct one. Despite crises, confusion, and fear, the first facts supporting this hopeful view can already be observed in some of the international research laboratories.

EIGHT | Work
in
Progress

I

The negotiations had been going on for hours. Cigarette smoke hung dense in the room. On one side of the long conference table, the representatives of CERN, showing signs of exhaustion and nervousness; on the other side, the Soviet scientists and officials. The subject of their discussions: future close cooperation between the large Geneva laboratory and the new research institute for high-energy physics in Prodvino, near Serpukhov. Several months earlier, on July 4, 1967, a treaty (prepared by Weisskopf) had been signed in Moscow by Professor Bernard Gregory, the present Director-General of CERN, and Professor A. Petrosiants, chairman of the State Commission for the Use of Atomic Energy. It constituted a proper pact between the partners for the joint use and development of the now most powerful accelerator in the world, the Big Machine of Prodvino.

The details of the agreement, which would soon require the continuous presence of sizable Western teams of machine physicists, technicians, electronics specialists, and nuclear physicists in the heart of the Soviet Union, had been left for "working parties" that were to meet later. Although both sides had made obvious efforts to come to terms, a number of difficult problems arose, as always happens during negotiations of international treaties, and some of them seemed almost insoluble. For example, who would be liable in case of damage to the CERN teams' delicate electronic instruments and "kicker" magnets during transportation to Serpukhov? Western insurance companies would accept responsibility only up to the Russian border. Then the Soviet authorities would have to take over. But that would require a thorough examination of the apparatus at the port of entry, and the act of examining, if not carried out by an expert, might produce the very damages one wished to avoid.

But that was actually one of the simpler problems. It was necessary to define the relations between the Soviet authorities and the foreigners to be involved in the construction of a system for fast ejection of the proton beam and the installation of radio-frequency separators. Would the foreigners be permitted to receive newspapers from their home countries, which were ordinarily prohibited in the Soviet Union? Could they count on their mail not being censored? What of their freedom of movement? Who would be liable in case of accidents on the job?

Empty soda bottles accumulated on the table. Ash trays overflowed. Western stomachs, unaccustomed to late Russian mealtimes, rumbled. Then, in the growing discomfort, a participant interjected: "Aren't we splitting hairs on the pelt of an unborn bear?"

The remark restored pleasantness to the atmosphere. Indeed, it was not at all clear at this point that the Big Machine, the 70 BeV monster on which Soviet physicists had been laboring for almost seven years, would actually function. The attempts to start up the new proton synchrotron (1,542 feet in diameter and almost a mile—4,867 feet—in circumference) during the visit of the CERN negotiators had thus far been unsuccessful. The deadline the builders had set for themselves was less than a month away. Since 1960 they had been aiming for their "giant" to take its first steps on November 7, 1967, at the latest, for that was the fiftieth anniversary of the great Revolution.

It was already October 13, and everyone was anxious about the impending final date. The negotiators were lunching in the Cafe Orbita, the new research city's restaurant decorated with rocket motifs, sawing their bear steaks, when Charles Peyrou of CERN jokingly said to his hosts: "I'll bet you're sorry now you started your Revolution so early."

II

In the middle of the following night Ludmilla Smirnova's telephone rang. She and her family had moved to Prodvino some time earlier, because her linguistic skills (and her charm) were needed in the new laboratory more than in Dubna, for dealing with foreign visitors.

"The telephone!" shouted the children, who had been awakened. "It's probably hooligans" (an expression incorporated into Russian for antisocial elements), murmured their mother, turning over and going back to sleep. In a few minutes the phone rang again. Later it rang a third time. Finally someone banged on the door: "Ludmilla, Ludmilla, quick! This is it!"

"How I got out of the house I'll never know," Smirnova told me a month later in Prodvino. "Outside, people were converging from everywhere. They were hurrying through the dark streets toward the main laboratory. The closer we got, the more crowded it became. We smiled at one another, but no one dared utter a word aloud, for it must have been about two in the morning."

Colin Ramm, there as a CERN negotiator, had just gone to bed when he was roused by a knock on the door.

"I knew immediately what had happened," he said. "Up until the time we went home to bed we had been watching the control room try to bring the beam up to full energy. Now they must have succeeded. The way people streamed out of all the houses, shook hands, embraced, and continued on arm in arm, the procession becoming longer and longer, made me think of the Pied Piper of Hamelin. I'm not ordinarily given to emotion, but when we stood there in the control room and watched the recording instruments show the beam climbing up to 60, 70, and then even to 76 billion—higher than the expected maximum—tears came to my eyes. We fell into one another's arms, probably even kissed, and naturally drank a little. Vodka, whiskey, later Crimean champagne. With it, coarse Russian black bread. That was certainly one of the great moments of my life."

Everybody celebrated until five in the morning, in the Cafe Orbita, at a long table made by pushing together many small ones.

A few hours later the negotiations were taken up again. "It is actually a nice fat bear we are dealing with now, wouldn't you say?" began one of the Russian speakers. A thunderous ovation expressed concurrence.

III

It was on an unseasonably mild November day that I journeyed for almost three hours, in one of the largest black limousines belonging to the Russian Atomic Energy Commission, to Serpukhov, on the main road leading to Kharkov and the Crimea. As soon as the completely new residential quarters in the southern part of Moscow, with their white and yellowish apartment houses, were behind us, the somber and yet lovely landscape of vast plains and birch woods, described so beautifully

207

by the nineteenth-century Russian writers, spread out ahead. Chekhov was the name of one of the small towns we drove through, but it is hard to imagine anything further removed from the spirit of the subtle writer than this careless conglomeration of crude flat-roofed barrack-like dwellings, with façades bearing the dirty tearstains of melting snow.

"We had to build quickly and poorly after the war, in order to provide shelter for all the homeless," my guide explained. "In this part of the country, south of Moscow, the Germans wreaked particular havoc." I was silent, ashamed of my criticism for esthetic reasons. I admired, all the more, the way nature heals the scars of war, by covering with a carpet of moss, in all shades of green, the ground that only yesterday had been tortured by the treads of tanks.

Sometime earlier, when I had applied to visit the new laboratory, the Soviet representative at the International Atomic Energy Agency in Vienna had said: "Those physicists! They have ruined one of the most beautiful landscapes in Russia with their project! Painters, poets, dreamers used to come to Serpukhov. I, myself, have always dreamed of having a *dacha* there. Gone. Protons have precedence."

I expected the worst. Fortunately, however, the new accelerator and its related settlement, Prodvino, have been so skillfully embedded in lofty pine forests that the natural beauty of the surroundings has been preserved. The builders of Prodvino belong to the young, post-Stalin generation. If one compared their settlement with Dubna, one would never think only one and a half decades had elapsed between the establishment of the old and the new "city of scientists"; it seemed more like one and a half centuries. Now, the last remnants of Russsian character are gone. The multistoried apartment houses, well-kept playgrounds, and shops with large windows could just as well be in a suburb of West Berlin, Paris, London, Amsterdam, or Geneva. They are functional, not entirely without elegance, and quite comfortable. It is not only the Big Machines all over the world that look alike, but the housing developments associated with them, too.

IV

Dr. Yves Goldschmidt-Clermont, one of the first CERN observers to visit Prodvino, gave the following description of the accelerator. "To our eyes, more familiar with the CERN and Brookhaven machines, the Serpukhov magnets and their supports appeared large and massive, the tunnel endless. Alice in Wonderland's mushroom that makes everything bigger is, in this case, partly the Russian engineering tradition and partly the factor of almost three in accelerator energy." The impression of hyperdimensionality of this now Biggest Machine was heightened even more, during my visit, by the fact that in the entire huge plant there was hardly a person to be seen. Evidently everyone was recovering from the anniversary celebrations that had just ended. After the weeks of strenuous labor that had culminated in starting the accelerator on schedule, the relaxing pause was only too well deserved.

The immense experimental hall that spans one part of the circular tunnel without a support must, by now, be populated with Soviet and foreign research teams. After several months of trials and breaking in, the first experiments were started at the same time as work was being continued on the development and improvement of the machine.

In contrast to Dubna's synchrophasotron, which has never measured up to the original expectations, the Serpukhov accelerator is, in the opinion of the experts (Western included), an extremely well-built, exact, and reliable instrument. "Everything runs like clockwork," I was told by Colin Ramm, whose standards of precision are notoriously high.

Doubtless the Soviet machine physicists are now more certain of their skills than they used to be. They have mastered the arts of beam handling and continuously increasing the beam intensity. Not only have they come up to the topmost Western levels but they have also developed some highly original concepts. Stimulating impulses radiate mostly from the Siberian institute for nuclear physics in Akademgorodok, headed by the imaginative, energetic, and determined nuclear physicist Gershon Budker. When he and his team visited the lab at Meyrin in the spring of 1967, *The* CERN *Courier* commented: "The particular attraction of this visit, which causes us to single it out from the steady flow of visits to CERN, lay in the great fund of new and daring approaches to the problems posed by accelerator technology, which have stemmed from this Novosibirsk team. . . . Ideas fly from this group like sparks from a grinding wheel. Almost certainly not all of them are destined to create a fire, but it has been a refreshing experience to encounter these unorthodox ideas."

Budker himself is of the opinion that some of his success can be attributed to the fact that he and his team take greater risks than the physicists in Big Science laboratories. More than once he did not hesitate to throw to the winds the opinions and warnings of conservative advisers. Even when a committee of "three wise men," set up by his teacher and friend Kurchatov, declared itself against his plan for a new type of storage ring in which electrons would be made to collide with their corresponding antimatter (positive electrons, or "positrons"), he was able to impose his will, and, in doing so, effected an important scientific breakthrough.

Budker's next project was to be a machine in which proton-antiproton collisions of 1,300 BeV would be generated with particle beams of 25 BeV. He estimated its probability of failure to be twenty percent. CERN, Brookhaven, and Serpukhov could not afford such a high margin of risk, Budker held, in a conversation with the English writer Robin Clarke. One explanation for the fact that Budker can take greater risks is that he has a considerable amount of economic independence. His institute near Novosibirsk produces "as a sideline" atomic research equipment that is sold all over the Soviet Union. The profits from this industry are put into new experiments.

"Why don't you do the same thing?" Budker is said to have once asked his American colleague Panofsky.

"We can't," sighed the Director of the Stanford Linear Accelerator Laboratory; "we don't live in a capitalist country."

V

Among American scientists living in the age of Big Science (as costly as it is unwieldy) the joy in the risk, the courage to venture into the untried, has also not yet died out. That became clear to the widespread family of high-energy physicists in a most dramatic way, when Robert Rathbun Wilson, Director of the newly established National Accelerator Laboratory, spoke before the Sixth International Conference on High-Energy Accelerators on September 12, 1967. The title of his talk was quite unexciting. It read: "Some Aspects of the 200 BeV Accelerator." But several days before Wilson had gone to the rostrum in the university town of Cambridge, Massachusetts, the almost three hundred conference participants knew that something special was in store for them.

Bob Wilson is a highly unusual personality among today's physicists. The last twenty years have turned many eminent scientists into "elder statesmen of science" who, with greater responsibility, increased power, and growing funds, have lost their fund of imagination, irreverence, and pleasure in experimentation. Not Wilson. Although he was one of the builders of Cornell University's Big Machines, he has remained a "tinkerer," a nonconformist by temperament and conviction, who doesn't give a fig for scientific prestige and status, and—the epitome of insubordination—cares even less about the almighty dollar.

Hardly a scientist today would decline the offer of millions of dollars in support of his laboratory. Yet that is exactly what

Wilson did in 1962. In his contribution to a volume honoring Hans Bethe on his sixtieth birthday, Wilson stated: "With barely a pause I picked up the phone, called the people in the National Science Foundation, and politely informed them that I was sorry, but no longer wanted their money. For people who had worked so hard for several years to secure funds for our 3 BeV machine, they were magnificent." The conversation was not the outcome of a dispute, as one might imagine. It was simply that the physicist, after some conferences with his closest collaborators, suddenly discovered that several ingenious technical improvements would enable them to raise the energy of their old accelerator to 2.2 BeV, inside of a year, for only $200,000. It seemed senseless, therefore, to spend the proffered $8 million on the construction of a new machine that would not be much more powerful (3 BeV) and for which, in addition, they would have to wait a good five years.

The result of this uncommon (and unorthodox) moderation was a high-level decision to grant this "white sheep" not his original $8 million, but $15 million, so that he could now build a "bargain" 10 BeV machine. Naturally, malicious tongues began to wag, claiming that was exactly what Wilson had had in mind from the beginning. He had only employed a more original strategy to draw the money out of the governmental coffers.

But those who are somewhat closer to this slim, sensitive scholar who, in his middle years, still looks like an enthusiastic student, know that he is among the rare few who believe that science is not furthered by unnecessary luxury but is, instead, seduced into spiritual indolence. He once stated: "If we had any secret in constructing machines cheaply and rapidly, that secret was our willingness, almost eagerness, to make mistakes. I have always maintained that something that works right away is overdesigned and consequently will have taken too long to build and will have cost too much."

The history of Wilson accelerators, by his own account, is as full of grotesque errors and setbacks, accidental and non-accidental breakdowns as an early Chaplin comedy. The head of the laboratory, who never hesitates to use a screwdriver, checks a damaged fuse. A tremendous flash blinds him. His eyebrows are singed. A great bang forces his hasty retreat. The tubing breaks, squirting oil all over him. Hydrogen, sucked in by a leak, explodes just as it comes out of a hot vacuum pump. An iron bar falls from a crane, missing the experimenter by a hair. To his mind, it was not a guardian angel who had spared him, but the laws of probability. Day and night, damages are repaired, tricks invented, methods improvised (which sometimes become recognized techniques later on). Everything is tested, nothing remains untried, until the stubborn apparatus yields and does what it is supposed to do.

The tired and toilworn team gathers around a completed machine. Wilson reports: "We all grimly assembled for the arduous task ahead. To our utter amazement, just as soon as the magnet was powered . . . a fat beam appeared before our unbelieving eyes. We are getting old, I thought. We have overdesigned and overbuilt! Even so we all retired to the nearest bar for a celebration—not knowing quite how to behave so early in the evening."

VI

It indicates a good deal of courage on the part of Robert Wilson that he took over the job of building the largest and costliest postwar project in nuclear physics. A number of more experienced machine builders have turned it down in view of obvious difficulties. Although the cost of the machine was estimated at $300 million, the Bureau of the Budget of the United States Government had hinted that the taxpayer could not be expected to pay much more than $240 million for the construction of this research tool, particularly in time of war. Furthermore, the site at Weston, Illinois, was not considered as very advantageous by most of the experts.

It indicates also a good deal of courage on the part of the United States Atomic Energy Commission that such an unusual, such a "wild," man was selected to head this project. Those who had backed Wilson, because they expected something exceptional from him, were not disappointed. When Wilson presented his version of the machine project to the Cambridge Conference, a number of new and bold ideas were added to the previous project of a 200 BeV machine. During the summer of 1967, aided by his team and consultants from other American laboratories, Wilson had worked out a tentative design which not only took into account the anticipated budget cuts, but also offered more possibilities for less money, namely, the option to increase the energy of the machine to 400-500 BeV later on.

How would he achieve this? On June 15, 1967, Wilson had gathered round him on the tenth floor of the Executive Plaza, a skyscraper in the Oak Brook Shopping Center west of Chicago, a small group of determined physicists and engineers. They examined carefully the previous design studies for Big Machines, such as the extensive studies made by the Berkeley group and the CERN study for a European 300 BeV machine. How could money be saved here and there, and how could an increase of energy be prepared for later? "We decided to spend the first two weeks wildly, by considering all sorts of far-out schemes," Wilson said. "However, on the last day of that period we buckled down and designed—in essentially one fell stroke—a separated-function machine which had a radius of five eighths of a mile."

The term "separated-function machine" expresses an important new feature of the American machine. The two functions, focusing and bending the proton beam, are performed by a single, very heavy, and expensive type of magnet in the older machines of CERN and Brookhaven and in the designs for the American 200 BeV and the European 300 BeV machines. The Oak Brook team, making use of the most sophisticated developments in magnet design, showed that, if the necessary functions are divided between two separate kinds of magnets—complicated quadrupole magnets and ordinary "window-frame" magnets—great savings would be made possible in these most expensive parts of an accelerator. On the basis of this innovation, the new machine would require much less steel than originally specified.

Then too, the size of the new magnets could be considerably reduced because of more efficient use of magnetic field volume, resulting, in turn, in a decrease in the dimensions of the circular tunnel, which would be smaller in volume by a factor of two and a half than according to the old design. Wilson also believes it will be possible to avoid anchoring the new machine in the ground, a procedure that had led to great expenditure in the case of the CERN machine. No piles would be sunk deep into the earth. The only foundation for the accelerator would be a thick slab of concrete embedded in the fields. ("A very simple system of stretched wires should provide a method of continuously monitoring and adjusting the radial and vertical positions of the magnets even if the ground should move.") Finally, there would be additional saving by cutting office and laboratory space to the absolute minimum, a step made necessary by the stringent expense limitations. It will make life harder for the future users but there is always a hope for more money for buildings later on.

How long will it take to build this machine? Wilson believes it can be done in less time than the previous plans called for. The earliest completion date he quotes is 1972; more careful estimates that allow for obstacles and postponements, mostly of a political nature, indicate that it will be 1973 or 1974 before the largest research laboratory in the United States will be completed.

On this subject, in discussions with his colleagues, Wilson remarked that he felt that the construction work should be done, as much as possible, under pressure. "When I think of this machine, first its construction, and then the work to be done with it, I realize how the years will pass. Last night I tried to imagine what it will be like when I want to do an experiment there one day. It suddenly occurred to me that at the age I will have reached by that time it will probably not be so easy for me to hobble from the administration building to the laboratories. And I had the horrible thought that by then I might need, more than a research assistant, a good nurse."

VII

When I met Bob Wilson in his temporary headquarters, the large room that occupies the entire tenth floor, almost without partitions, of the Oak Brook skyscraper, I was amazed at how unusually sensitive and mobile his face was. He had more of the artist or the philosopher about him than the scientist, for he seemed impressionable and open to suggestion; quite the opposite of the brash American, the energetic, outer-directed man who gets things done. I had heard that this famous machine builder paints and sculpts—well enough to be a professional. His deep interest in architecture was new to me, however. He told me that after the war he had devoted a considerable amount of time to the great European cathedrals and their builders, had seen everything and read everything he could get hold of on the subject. First Adams, then Bernardini, Faissner, Powell, Weisskopf, and now another high-energy physicist was pointing out to me the spiritual affinity of his work to that of the anonymous builders of the medieval churches—and that with an intensity almost like religious fervor.

He handed me a reprint of an article he had written ten years ago for *Scientific American* in which he had stated: "It seems to me that the designer of an accelerator is moved by much the same spirit which motivated the designer of a cathedral. The esthetic appeal of both structures is primarily technological. . . . In the accelerator we feel a technological esthetic—the spirality of the orbits of the particles, the balance of electrical and mechanical motion, the upward surge of forces and events until an ultimate of height is reached, this time in the energy of the particles."

In another American magazine, *International Science and Technology,* Wilson once told of the thrill of working on an accelerator, the pleasure to be derived from unexpected findings, the exaltation experienced when an experiment succeeds at last. Now, he did not care to talk much more about the subject, fearing that dwelling too long on those rare and precious experiences might spoil them. Inspiration comes when one least expects it. He had had one of his best ideas when, in Paris between flights, he had gone to the Grande Chaumière, where one can join a life drawing class for a few francs.

"Suddenly I noticed the man next to me staring at my sheet of paper," he said. "Only then did I realize what I had drawn. It was not a portrait of one of the—incidentally quite comely—models on the platform, but the ground plan of a new type of accelerator."

VIII

Every morning between nine and ten, Wilson meets with his collaborators in a corner of the large room in Oak Brook, while work goes on in other sections. He stands before the blackboard, in a white shirt, sleeves rolled up, and confers with his main team in so nonchalant a manner that one would never get the impression that important decisions are being made. Soon the meeting is over, and an entirely informal debate ensues on a storage ring project, for which eminent physicists from all parts of the country and abroad have come to this suburb of Chicago. Some have traveled thousands of miles to talk shop with their colleagues for only one or two hours, and will be home again by evening. They come without formal invitation, for Wilson dislikes "programmed meetings." He believes one meets too many people there who view participation as some kind of status symbol. He trusts that word will get around, in any case, that "exciting things" are going on in Oak Brook.

Wilson is cognizant of the great disappointment his colleagues in Berkeley and Brookhaven—who had hoped to build the new Big Machine near their own laboratories—must have felt a first on his appointment and the selection of the site near Chicago. "But now they are all taking part as if it was their own cause," said Ed Goldwasser, Wilson's right-hand man. His boss added: "We solved the perennial visitor problem that makes life so hard in other laboratories. We don't let visitors disturb us, we simply put them to work. The number of people has been so large that I cannot even try to give proper credit—but I hope" —and here he almost visibly put his tongue into his cheek— "that will be done in future publications by the contributors themselves."

Another human-relations problem, one occupying the physicists involved in the preparation of the new accelerator, is less easy to solve. They are all decided opponents of segregation. In Illinois, where the new machine is to be built, however, there is no open-housing legislation that would give Negroes the right to purchase homes near Weston or even to rent apartments there. Prominent Senators, led by John O. Pastore of Rhode Island, declared in debates on budget authorization that they would oppose the project as long as Illinois refused to relinquish its discriminatory practices. The physicists find themselves in the paradoxical situation, therefore, of having as their political friends the foes of their research project.

As has been demonstrated by CERN, and by increasing collaboration between Eastern and Western laboratories, Big Science projects can further politically desirable developments. However, political factors can impede scientific progress, and the larger and more costly the project the more dependent it is on elements outside science.

The decision that the American Big Machine be built, not in the vicinity of Denver (and its magnificent ski slopes) or in sunny California, as most physicists supposedly had hoped, but in the Midwest, with its windy winters and muggy summers, was made on political grounds. That some Congressmen spoke against appropriations for the machine also had political motives.

The physicist Norman Ramsey, President of the University Research Association (made up of forty universities and institutions that are to support the National Accelerator Laboratory), devoted his entire address at the Cambridge conference to the financial and political constraints with which high-energy physics had to cope. He spoke out of the proper realization that nonscientific social factors are among the parameters to be considered in the construction of accelerators.

"As the magnitudes of the accelerator projects increase, they become major national problems, and, as a result, in the considerations of governmental authorities, they may become coupled to other major national problems which may seem quite unrelated. Thus the appropriation for the SLAC (Stanford Linear Accelerator Laboratory) was delayed a year because of a Hanford production reactor, which in turn was involved in the question of public versus private power. . . . It would not surprise me if the final negotiations for the 300 BeV European accelerator should become involved with such European questions as the Common Market."

IX

When the members of the Conseil, the "government" of CERN, concluded the last of their quarterly meetings in the middle of December, 1967, they must have felt like the family finally about to take the trip it had been planning down to the most minute detail for years, and then at the last minute is prevented from leaving. Even at the summer session in June, hopes had still been high that the starting signal for the new 300 BeV Big Machine, under preparation for so many years, would be given.

At that time CERN had issued voluminous material in which the design studies made in 1963 and 1964 for the European accelerator had been revised and brought up to date in the light of the latest developments. The closing sentences of a public announcement had read: "The altered time schedule is based on the expectation that the principal decisions concerning the project will be made by the end of 1967. The building site should be accessible by the middle of 1968. The construction group would be set up at the same time, and building could commence by the middle of 1969. Provided that these dates are adhered to, the research program could be initiated at the beginning of 1977."

Now, everything had been overturned. New time schedules had to be instituted, new estimates made, and new conferences arranged with the key personnel assigned to construction of the new machine, for it was not at all certain they would not revise their own plans and take other positions.

Although CERN had missed an extremely important deadline, the tone of the meeting was "cheerful, even optimistic," according to the British magazine *Nature,* a fact that might be attributed to the Conseil members having come to Geneva expecting even worse: a death sentence, recommendation by one government or another that the entire project be abandoned.

Better late than never may have been their consolation. In the course of the next few years some of the political objections and some of the recent technical objections to the 300 BeV machine might be dispelled.

"Politics, the New Force in Physics" (the title of an article on the increasing influence of political problems on physics research, by V. K. McElheny, the European correspondent of *Science*) had been affecting the construction plans of CERN in a multitude of ways since 1966. Heading the list were the slowing down of the economic boom and the growing burden of social welfare expenditures for European governments. A role by no means negligible was played by the British economic crisis of 1967. Finally, the crisis within the European organizations, precipitated mainly by President de Gaulle, could not be prevented from having repercussions on "Europe's model institution," CERN.

France has been suspected recently of deliberately playing power politics with science, with bubble chambers taking the part of cruisers and television patents that of machine guns. For some time the general opinion had been that the 45 BeV "national accelerator" project, announced on several occasions by French physicists, had only been a pretext to influence the selection of the site for the Big Machine in favor of France. But in 1966, and even more in 1967, the dominant view was that this accelerator was not considered merely a "bargaining point" in Saclay, but there was definite intent to build it, and the first three hundred million new francs for the initial building stages could be expected by 1968, at the latest.

The Germans, too, began to speak more often about constructing their own large proton synchrotron. W. Heintz, a physicist at the Karlsruhe Reactor Center, presented detailed plans for a 40 BeV machine, at the Sixth Accelerator Conference in Cambridge, England. The German scientist, and a French speaker as well, were sharply criticized by Dzhelepov (USSR), Green (U.S.), and Amaldi (Italy, chairman of the design group for the European 300 BeV machine) on the grounds that hardly anything new could come of machines in this medium range and therefore their construction was meaningless. But the criticism had little effect. Just as some years ago the failure to form a European defense alliance had led to an intensification in national armaments, the present deadlock on a joint scientific project threatened to result in a return to scientific nationalism.

Is this development to be halted? There are both optimists and pessimists in the community of European physicists, as there are everywhere. At the moment, there is greater justification for believing that the drama of the European Big Machine will yet have a happy ending. The first discoveries made with the 76 BeV Serpukhov machine might well stimulate the Western teams participating in the experiments to build an instrument of their own, powerful enough to make further advances. But that could be done only by their countries' uniting in a communal effort.

X

It is not surprising that the governments are reluctant to embark on a new venture of building another giant accelerator for Europe, ten times larger than the one at Geneva. Is it not risking too much when such large amounts of money and manpower are sunk into one single scientific venture? Scientists in other fields are already growing envious of the particle physicists and are asking for equivalent support for their own projects. Who knows whether these giant accelerators will work well enough, or bring about new results which are commensurate with the enormous expense? What representative or minister would dare to justify losses of many millions if the instruments on which they were spent failed to work, even temporarily or in part?

And yet the history of scientific progress has repeatedly shown that setbacks are inevitable, and the initial failure of an unusual and audacious experiment tends to be more productive than the success derived from pursuing an established line.

Only when the scientist is permitted to make mistakes, even in the age of Big Science, will it be possible for him to proceed through trial and error to the disclosure of new horizons. If "efficiency" is demanded, or if results must be known in advance, then the human spirit will descend to a bookkeeping mentality.

A way out of the dilemma is indicated by the ideas of Stephen Toulmin, a British historian of ideas, now teaching in the United States at Brandeis University. At the end of 1966, in a stimulating contribution to a debate on the problems of scientific development ("Culture, Overheads or Tertiary Industry"), he pointed out that the focal problem in the age to come will not be production and its costs, but employment. "More and more in the decades ahead, we shall be free to occupy ourselves with pure science and be *happy* to do so. . . . We are in a situation in which maintenance of employment is socially more important than sheer productivity alone . . . ," he writes, and goes on to state that John Maynard Keynes had predicted, as early as 1930, in a treatise entitled "Economic Possibilities for Our Grandchildren," that even before the end of the century we would be faced with the choice of "cither to employ men in producing unwanted goods, or to find some other range of activities in which to occupy them. The drudgery of production could . . . yield place to more creative occupations."

Toulmin writes: "Pure scientific research is, and can deliberately be chosen to be, one of those new tertiary activities by which employment and prosperity can be maintained in an industrial society, even after both primary and secondary industries (agriculture and manufacture) have become *too efficient* to occupy the available labor force. A scientific research laboratory can serve, just as well as a manufacturing enterprise, as the focus around which the life and prosperity of a community can be organized. To hazard a social prophecy, one can well imagine the 'laboratory town' becoming as characteristic a feature of late twentieth century social life as the 'mill town' was in the mid-nineteenth century."

Seen as a "tertiary industry," a research laboratory would no longer be required to produce results that might have later practical applications. It would simply produce satisfaction for hundreds of thousands of people who find worthwhile and meaningful occupations there. In the "post-production" and "post-manufacture" era the quality of life will be the goal of society, and that implies a creative culture developing artistically as well as scientifically. In that culture, it will not be the financial costs but the esthetic or intellectual worth of a new creation, and the spiritual satisfaction to be derived from work on it, that will become the criteria for its furtherance by the community. The beliefs of yesterday and today in the possession of material goods, or war, could then be replaced by more meaningful values.

I received unexpected confirmation of Toulmin's vision during my visit to the Russian laboratory town of Prodvino that has grown around the large 76 BeV accelerator. The young woman teacher from the easternmost regions of the Soviet Union, Director of the new House of Culture in Prodvino, told me that a group of physicists and technicians were rehearsing every evening for a New Year's revue they were composing. The theme and title of the show had finally been settled upon. It was "Gods, Men and Machines."

The first act takes place on Mount Olympus. Gods and heroes are discussing what to give to the inhabitants of the world soon to be created. Mars, who is to put victory-promising weapons into their hands, and Atlas, who is to give them the enjoyment of physical labor, can test their ideas. Only when the people, exhausted by war and drudgery, protest, is it Minerva's turn to be heard. And she presents the people with a huge accelerator —could it have been anything else, in Prodvino?—so that they can find fulfillment in the search for truth.

Soon afterward, the principal of the new school in Prodvino touched upon the same theme, as he guided me around the spacious premises where the children of the machine builders, researchers, and technicians are trained for living. His remarks were prompted by an exhibition displayed in the corridors, lobbies, and niches of the school building, which was devoted to the "heroic deeds of the 60th Army in the great patriotic war." Twenty years before construction was started on the Big Machine and its adjacent settlement, those troops had defended the piece of ground we were standing on, and the neighboring factory town of Serpukhov, in terrible battles that raged for years against Hitler's divisions.

In laying the road beds and electrical cables, and in excavating the accelerator tunnel, the workers had again and again come upon skeletons, shell splinters, corroded weapons, and moldy scraps of uniforms. Part of these findings—bits of flags, steel helmets, captured cannons, leaflets, documents, and photographs —were now gathered in this small school museum. The teacher, about fifty years of age, showed me the collection without a trace of pride. "Every inch of soil here was soaked with blood," he said. "It was a frightful time." He spoke of it in the detached tone of an archeologist, familiar with the barbaric customs of the past only through books, discussing excavations from ancient history.

Suddenly he stopped in front of one of the many slightly faded photographs. It showed a very young officer with close-cropped hair, wearing his many medals with tremendous self-confidence.

"Do you know who that is?" he asked.

He answered by pointing to himself.

"I've grown old, haven't I? Well, about a thousand years have passed since that time. Now we live in an entirely different world. Don't you agree?"

He looked at me once more. On his face was written hope, but also anxiety.

"Don't you agree?" he insisted.

SELECTED BIBLIOGRAPHY

"To dig deeper"—this is the heading of a column in the American journal *International Science and Technology*, listing references to articles and books which enable the reader to acquire a deeper and broader knowledge of the subjects covered in each issue.

In an era in which the flood of information is getting more and more out of hand, the idea seems to me to be worth imitating. Therefore I should like to mention literature that was helpful to me in writing this book, in the hope that some readers will find these references of use.

THE HISTORY OF NUCLEAR PHYSICS

Bernstein, J. "A Question of Parity," *The New Yorker*, May 12, 1962.

Cline, B. L. *The Questioners*. New York: Thomas Y. Crowell Company, 1965.

Gamow, G. *Thirty Years That Shook Physics*. New York: Doubleday & Company, Inc., 1966.

Hanson, N. R. *Patterns of Discovery*. New York: Cambridge University Press, 1958.

Hoffmann, B. *The Strange Story of the Quantum*. London: Penguin Books Ltd., 1963.

Medawar, P. B., O. R. Frisch, *et al. Experiment*. London: BBC Publication, 1964.

Moore, Ruth. *Niels Bohr*. New York: Alfred A. Knopf, Inc., 1966.

Oppenheimer, R. "Physics and Man's Understanding." *Encounter*, April, 1966.

Toulmin, S., and J. Goodfield. *The Architecture of Matter*. New York: Harper & Row, 1963.

Weisskopf, V. F. *Knowledge and Wonder*. New York: Doubleday & Company, Inc., 1962.

Wilson, Robert R. *Perspectives in Modern Physics*. New York: Interscience Publishers, Inc., 1966.

DISCUSSIONS OF RESEARCH AND TECHNOLOGY

Auger, P. "Limits to Science," *New Scientist*, September 24, 1964.

Bronowski, J. "The Machinery of Nature," *Encounter*, November, 1965.

——. *Science and Human Values*. New York: Harper & Row, 1965 (Revised edition).

Gerlach, W. *Humanität und naturwissenschaftliche Forschung*, Brunswick, Friedrich Vieweg & Sohn, 1962.

Green, M. *Science and the Shabby Curate of Poetry.* New York: W. W. Norton & Company, Inc., 1965.

Heisenberg, W. *Physics and Philosophy.* New York: Harper & Row, 1958.

Heitler, W. *Der Mensch und die naturwissenschaftliche Erkenntnis.* Brunswick, Friedrich Vieweg & Sohn, 1961.

Hogben, L. *Science in Authority.* New York: Humanities Press, 1963.

Holton, G. (ed.) *Science and Culture.* Boston: Houghton Mifflin Company, 1965.

Kuhn, T. S. *The Structure of Scientific Revolutions.* University of Chicago Press, 1962.

Marcuse, H. *One Dimensional Man.* Boston: Beacon Press, 1964.

Margenau, H. *The New Style of Science.* New Haven: Groton School Press, 1964.

Ozbekhan, H. *Technology and Man's Future.* Santa Monica, Calif.: System Development Corp., 1966.

Popper, K. R. *The Poverty of Historicism.* New York: Basic Books, Inc., 1966.

Powell, C. F. "The Role of Pure Science in European Civilization," *Physics Today,* May, 1965.

Wagner, F. *Die Wissenschaft und die gefährdete Welt.* Munich: C. H. Beck, 1964.

Weisskopf, V. F. "Why Pure Science?" *Bulletin of the Atomic Scientists,* April, 1965.

Yuan, C. C. L., *et al.* "The Nature of Matter," Brookhaven, 1965.

High Energy Physics Program: Report on National Policy and Background Information, 89th Congress, Washington, 1965.

High Energy Physics Research: Hearings before the Subcommittee on Research, Development and Radiation of the Joint Committee on Atomic Energy, 89th Congress, Washington, 1965.

SCIENCE AND SOCIETY

Arendt, H. *Vita Activa.* Stuttgart: W. Kohlhammer Verlag, 1960.

Bernal, J. D. *The Social Function of Science.* Cambridge, Mass.: The M.I.T. Press, 1967.

Born, M. *Von der Verantwortung des Naturwissenschaftlers.* Munich: Nymphenburger Verlagshandlung, 1965.

Bundy, McG. "The Scientist and National Policy," *Science,* March 1, 1963.

Buzzati-Traverso, A. A. "Scientific Research: The Case for International Support," *Science,* June 11, 1965.

Cockroft, J. "Scientific Collaboration in Europe," *New Scientist,* January 24, 1963.

Crozier, M. *Bureaucratic Phenomenon.* University of Chicago Press, 1964.

SELECTED BIBLIOGRAPHY

Escoffier-Lambiotte, M. "Science, Ethique et Culture dans la Société Moderne" (Interview with Professor Monod and Professor Jacob). *Le Monde*, December 9, 1965.

Fischer, E. *The Necessity of Art*. Baltimore: Penguin Books, Inc., 1964.

Greenberg, Daniel S. "The Politics of Pure Science," *Saturday Review*, November 4, 1967.

Greenfield, M. "Science Goes to Washington," *The Reporter*, September 26, 1963.

Grodzins, M., and E. Rabinowich (eds.). *The Atomic Age*. New York: Basic Books, Inc., 1963.

Hutchins, R., *et al. Science, Scientists and Politics*. Santa Barbara: Center for the Study of Democratic Institutions, 1963.

Klaw, S. "The Nationalization of U.S. Science," *Fortune*, September, 1964.

Meynaud, J., and B. Schröder. *Les Savants dans la Vie Internationale*. Paris: Editions Payot, 1962.

Ramsey, Norman F. "Support of High Energy Physics." Paper presented at the International Conference on High Energy Physics, Cambridge, Mass., 1960.

Salomon, J. J. "Science and Foreign Policy in Europe." (Address before the Swedish Royal Academy of Sciences). Stockholm: February 21, 1964.

Topchiev, A. V. "Science and Society," *Bulletin of the Atomic Scientists*, March, 1963.

Toulmin, Stephen. "Culture, Overheads or Tertiary Industry," *Minerva*, Vol. IV, No. 2, Winter, 1966.

Toynbee, A. "Die gegenwärtigen weltgeschichtlichen Entscheidungen und die Wissenschaft," *Universitas*, October, 1963.

Bulletin of the Atomic Scientists, 1954-1965, Chicago.

The Economic and Social Council Resolution No. 22 (III), October 3, 1964 (document E/233): "The Question of Establishing United Nations Research Laboratories," Lake Success, December, 1948.

Report of the Committee of Scientific Experts on International Research Laboratories, Economic and Social Council documents E/1694 and E/1694/Add. 1, August 10, 1948.

"Science and Technology in Contemporary Society," *Daedalus*, Spring, 1962.

Organisations Scientifiques Internationales, Vol. II. OCDE, Paris, 1963.

UNESCO and International Scientific Co-operation, UNESCO Report NS/ROU/43, Paris, January 15, 1964.

THE SCIENCE OF SCIENCE

Auger, P., G. Holton, *et al.* "Vers une synthèse dans l'organisation de la recherche scientifique," *Impact* (UNESCO) No. 1, 1966.

229

Bahrdt, H. P. "Soziologische Probleme der Big Science." Bremen: Rundbrief der Vereinigung deutscher Wissenschaftler, January, 1966.

Barber, B. *Science and the Social Order*. New York: Collier Books, 1952.

Barber, B., and W. Hirsch (eds.). *The Sociology of Science*. New York: The Macmillan Company, 1962.

Bernal, J. D. *Science in History*. New York: Hawthorn Books, Inc., 1965.

Cockroft, J., *et al. The Organization of Research Establishments*. New York: Cambridge University Press, 1966.

Colburn, R. "The Pleasures of Physics; Interview with Robert R. Wilson," *International Science and Technology*, May, 1965.

Cooper, W. W., *et al. New Perspectives in Organization Research*. New York: John Wiley & Sons, Inc., 1964.

Dedijer, S. "Research the Motor of Progress," *Bulletin of the Atomic Scientists*, June, 1962.

Eiduson, B. T. *Scientists—Their Psychological World*. New York: Basic Books, Inc., 1962.

Gentner, W. *Individuum und Kollektiv im modernen Forschungslaboratorium*. Heidelberg: Max-Planck-Institut für Kernphysik, 1964.

Goldsmith, M. (ed.). *The Science of Science*. London: Souvenir Press Ltd., 1965.

Hagstrom, W. O. *The Scientific Community*. New York: Basic Books, Inc., 1965.

Haskins, C. P. "Scientific Choice and the Individual," President's Report Year Book 63, 1963-64, Carnegie Institution of Washington.

Hine, M. G. N. *Financing High Energy Physics*. Geneva: CERN Information Service, May, 1964.

Klages, H., and H. W. Hetzler. "Entwicklungswege der Forschungsorganisation," *Humanismus und Technik*, Vol. 10, July, 1965.

Kowarski, L. *An Observer's Account of User Relations in the U.S. Accelerator Laboratories*. Geneva: CERN Publication 67-4, January, 1967.

————. "Psychology and Structure of Large Scale Physical Research," *Bulletin of the Atomic Scientists*, May, 1949.

Lapp, Ralph E. *The New Priesthood*. New York: Harper & Row, 1965.

Maddox, J. "Choice and the Scientific Community," *Minerva*, Winter, 1964.

Michaelis, M. "Obstacles to Innovation," *International Science and Technology*, November, 1964.

Moles, A. A. *La Creation Scientifique*. Geneva: Kister Editions S. A., 1957.

Policard, A. "The Life of the Team," *Impact*, Vol. XV, No. 1, 1965.

Presthus, R. *The Organizational Society*. New York: Random House (Vintage Books), 1962.

SELECTED BIBLIOGRAPHY

Price, D. J. de Solla. *Little Science, Big Science.* New York: Columbia University Press, 1963.

Townes, C. H. "Doing Research," *International Science and Technology,* March, 1964.

Weinberg, A. "The Coming Changes in American Science," *Science,* Vol. 142, No. 3591, 1963.

————. "Criteria for Scientific Choice," *Minerva,* Winter, 1963.

————. "Impact of Large-Scale Science on the United States," *Science,* vol. 134, No. 3473, 1961.

———— and V. F. Weisskopf. "Two Open Letters," *Physics Today,* June, 1964.

"Creativity and Learning," *Daedalus,* Summer, 1965.

Round Table Discussion on High Energy Physics, *Physics Today,* June, 1964.

CERN

Not in print:

Letters, directives, and reports from the early days of CERN (1949/50 to 1959).

(1) Archives of UNESCO, Paris.

(2) Private files of Pierre Auger, Paris.

In print or reproduced:

Amaldi, E. "But et Développement du CERN 1950-1954," Lecture, July, 1954, Varenna. Geneva: CERN Rep. 55-1 (reprod.)

Anthoine, R. "Le CERN et son grand Synchrotron à protons," *Industrie,* May, 1960.

————. "High Energy Physics Research at CERN," *Nuclear Engineering,* December, 1964.

Bernstein, J. "CERN," *The New Yorker,* December 12, 1964.

Brunner, A. "Zehn Jahre CERN," *Neue Zürcher Zeitung,* July 2, 1964.

Kowarski, L. "An Account of the Origin and the Beginnings of CERN." Geneva: CERN (reprod.) April 10, 1961.

Martin, C. N. "Visite au Centre Européen de Recherche Nucléaire," *Le Figaro Littéraire,* April 9-16, 1964.

Weisskopf, V. F. "What is CERN for?" Speech before Parliamentary and Scientific Commission, London, February, 1963. (See also CERN *Courrier,* September, 1963—abridged version.)

Annual Reports of the European Organization for Nuclear Research (CERN), Geneva 1955-65.

"CERN: An Opportunity in High Energy Physics," *Nature,* February 26, 1966.

CERN *Computer Newsletter* Nos. 1-6, Geneva, 1966.

CERN *Courrier,* 1959—June, 1966.

CERN 31st Session of the Council Draft Minutes (Farewell to Director-General V. F. Weisskopf), CERN/634, April, 1966.
Journal de l'Association du Personnel (CERN), 1956-65.
Procès-Verbaux du CERN 1952-54, CERN/Gen. 1-15, Rome.

RESEARCH IN THE EASTERN BLOC

Barbier, M. "La Recherche en Union Soviétique (La Physique des hautes énergies)," *Industries atomiques*, Nos. 11/12, 1963.

Barnier, L. *A quoi rêvent les savants sovietiques*. Paris: Editeurs Français Reunis, 1958.

Birjukov, W. A., M. M. Lebedenko, and A. M. Ryshov. *The Joint Institute for Nuclear Research in Dubna* (with a list of publications by the members of the Joint Institute: March, 1956, to March, 1959). Leipzig: Verlage der Wissenschaften, 1960.

Buchholz, A. *Neue Wege sowjetischer Bildung und Wissenschaft*. Cologne: Verlag Wissenschaft und Politik, 1963.

Cantacuzene, J. "A Novosibirsk . . . ," *Le Monde*, May 8-10, 1966.

Clarke, Robin. "Akademgorodok," *Science Journal*, August, 1967.

Gould, S. H. (ed.) *Sciences in Communist China*. Washington, D.C.: American Association for the Advancement of Science, 1961.

Jonas, A. M. "Atomic Energy in Soviet Bloc Nations," *Bulletin of the Atomic Scientists*, November, 1959.

Lewytzkyi, B. "Ideologie und Wissenschaft in der Sowjetunion," *Atomzeitalter*, July, 1964.

Müller-Markus, S. *Einstein und die Sowjetphilosophie*. Vol. 1. New York: Humanities Press, 1960.

————. "Physik gegen Diamat," *Wort und Wahrheit*, February, 1962.

Vichney, N. "La faucille, le marteau et la règle à calcul," *Le Monde*, series of articles, June 24-29, 1966.

Yurev, G. V. "Controversy Continues over Intellectual Opposition in Soviet Society," *Soviet Affairs Analysis Service*, 1963.

"China's Struggle to Catch Up in Science," *Business Week*, February 5, 1966.

"The Disciples of Archimedes Live!" (notes on the young scientists in Siberia), *Molodja gwardija*, No. 1, 1964 (compare *Ost-Probleme*, March 20, 1964).

"Methodological Problems of the Natural and Social Sciences," Proceedings of the Academy of Sciences, *Westnik Akademii nauk SSR*, Nr. 11, 1963 (compare *Ost-Probleme*, March 6, 1964).

Osteuropa-Naturwissenschaften 1961-65.

"Report on Soviet Science," special edition, *Survey*, July, 1964.

"Thirty Years After" (Kapitza's Visit to Great Britain), *Nature*, April 30, 1966.

SELECTED BIBLIOGRAPHY

INSTRUMENTS OF NUCLEAR RESEARCH

Accelerators

Adams, J. B. "Some Engineering Problems of the CERN Proton Synchrotron," *Discovery*, July, 1957.

Blewett, J. P., and M. S. Livingston. *Particle Accelerators*. New York: McGraw-Hill Book Company, 1962.

Burhop, E. H. S. "Discussions on Future High Energy Accelerators in Europe," CERN *Courrier*, February, 1964.

Decae, A. E. "Precision Survey of the 28 BeV Synchrotron in the European Organization for Nuclear Research," Reproduction from *Empire Survey Review*, London, 1961.

Livingston, M. S. *High-Energy Accelerators*. New York: John Wiley & Sons, Inc., 1956.

Regenstreif, E. *Le Synchrotron à Protons du* CERN. 3 vols. Geneva: CERN 59-66, 1959 (reprod.).

Yuan, L. C. L., and J. P. Blewett (eds.). "Experimental Program Requirements for a 300 to 1000 BeV Accelerator and Design Study for a 300 to 1000 BeV Accelerator." Brookhaven Publication, BNL, 772, December, 1962.

"Future Program for the CERN PS and Brookhaven AGS," Minutes of a Meeting, Brookhaven, September 10-14, 1962.

"Reports of the Working Party on the European High Energy Accelerator Program," CERN, 1963 and 1967.

Sites for the Proposed CERN *300 GeV Proton Synchrotron*. 2 vols. Geneva: CERN, 1967.

Detectors

Glaser, D. A. "The Bubble Chamber," *Scientific American*, February, 1955.

O'Neil, G. K. "The Spark Chamber," *Scientific American*, August, 1962.

Yagoda, H. "The Tracks of Nuclear Particles," *Scientific American*, May, 1956.

Scanning and Data Processing Devices

Macleod, G. R. *The Development of Data Analysis Systems for Bubble Chambers*. Geneva: CERN, July, 1962 (reprod.).

Spinrad, R. J. "The Computer and You," *Physics Today*, December, 1965.

Totaro, J. Burt. "The CDC 6000 Series," *Data Processing Magazine*, No. 3, 1966.

THE NEUTRINO
(in chronological order)

Faissner, H., *et al.* "The CERN Neutrino Spark Chamber," *Nuclear Instruments and Methods*, 20, 1963.

van der Meer, S., *et al.* "Magnetic Horn and Neutrino Flux Calculations," (Paper submitted at the International Conference, Siena, September, 1963), CERN NP/Int 63-26 (reprod.).

Gaillard, J. M. "CERN Neutrino Experiment" (Invited paper presented at the American Physical Society Meeting, New York, January, 1964), CERN 8435/p/eps (reprod.).

Bernardini, G. "Some Motivations for a Very Costly Long Range Program on High-Energy Neutrino Physics at CERN," *Proceedings of the Royal Society,* Vol. 278, London, 1964.

Gatto, R. "The Two Neutrinos," CERN 4214/kw (reprod.).

L'Etude des Neutrinos, CERN Information Service, January 28, 1965.

Perkins, D. H. "Tracking the Neutrinos (Experimental Physics with Neutrinos Conference, Geneva, January, 1965), *Science Journal,* April, 1965.

Plass, G. A Review for the CERN Conference on Experimental Neutrino Physics (manuscript), Geneva, CERN, 1965.

Reines, F., and J. P. F. Sellschop. "Neutrinos from the Atmosphere and Beyond," *Scientific American,* February, 1966.

ELEMENTARY PARTICLES
(articles selected for understandability)

Charpak, J. M. "Towards the Quark," *Discovery,* June, 1965.

Hine, Marvin G. N., and E. H. S. Burhop. "The 300 GeV Accelerator," *Science Journal,* July, 1967.

Feynman, R. The Feynman Lectures on Physics (lecture notes), 1964 (reprod.).

Weisskopf, V. F. "Quantum Theory and Elementary Particles," *Science,* Vol. 149, No. 3689, 1965.

Wilson, Robert R. "Particle Accelerators," *Scientific American,* March, 1958.

———. "Some Aspects of the 200 GeV Accelerator," International Conference on High Energy Accelerators, Cambridge, Mass., November, 1967.

Yang, Chen Ning. *Elementary Particles.* Princeton University Press, 1962.

"The Quantum Ladder, An Interview with Victor F. Weisskopf," *International Science and Technology,* June, 1963.

ACKNOWLEDGMENTS

The layman who undertakes the task of describing international research institutions and their problems depends, to a great extent, on the cooperation, and especially the patience, of his informants. For, without their guidance, he would be completely lost in these unfamiliar and unusual surroundings.

Scientists have often been accused (and not entirely unjustly) of being reserved toward journalists, for fear of being misunderstood. My experience, during the preparation of this work, has been that their attitude has been undergoing a marked change. I would like to call attention to this fact, particularly since my book is concerned mainly with the relations between scientists and the public.

First I should like to thank V. F. Weisskopf, Director-General of CERN from 1961 to 1965, for his advice and his critical comments, which were helpful indeed. Second, I should like to credit my old friend and colleague, G. H. Martin, editor-in-chief of the *Tribune de Genève*, with having given me the idea of writing a journalistic report on the European nuclear research institution near Geneva. Also, when I was about to abandon the project, because it seemed impossible to make such difficult material intelligible to the general public, he did not lose faith in the possibility of the undertaking and the necessity for it. Finally, I should like to express my gratitude to the following members of the world's three largest nuclear research laboratories, who were especially helpful to this inquisitive intruder:

CERN (FOUNDERS)

E. Amaldi (Italy), P. Auger (France), W. Heisenberg (German Federal Republic), L. Kowarski (France), J. Mussard (France), I. I. Rabi (U.S.A.)

CERN (FORMER AND PRESENT MEMBERS)

J. B. Adams (Great Britain), R. Anthoine (Belgium), R. Budde (German Federal Republic), H. Faissner (German Federal Republic), W. Gentner (German Federal Republic), A. G. Hester (Great Britain), G. Konreid (Great Britain), Ch. Peyrou (France), I. I. Rabi (U.S.A.), M. Sutherland (Great Britain), C. Tièche (Switzerland), K. M. Vahlbruch (German Federal Republic), H. W. Wachsmuth (German Federal Republic), H. Weigelt (German Federal Republic), H. Yoshiki (Japan), A. Zichichi (Italy)

THE BIG MACHINE

JOINT INSTITUTE FOR NUCLEAR RESEARCH

H. Barwich (formerly German Democratic Republic), D. I. Blochintzev (USSR), L. I. Lapidus (USSR), J. Schwanjev (USSR)

BROOKHAVEN NATIONAL LABORATORY

J. P. Blewett

I received valuable information also from the following persons:

CERN (FORMER AND PRESENT MEMBERS)

G. Augsburger (Switzerland), J. Baarli (Norway), G. Bernardini (Italy), H. Bethe (U.S.A.), F. Briandet (France), A. Burger (German Federal Republic), H. Burmeister (German Federal Republic), H. Coblans (Great Britain), G. Cocconi (Italy), G. von Dardel (Sweden), G. Domokosch (Hungary), G. V. Efimoy (USSR), G. Fidecaro (Italy), E. Fischer (German Federal Republic), J. A. Geibel (German Federal Republic), P. Germain (Belgium), J. Gervaise (France), Y. Goldschmidt-Clermont (Belgium), B. P. Gregory (France), A. Günther (German Federal Republic), G. H. Hampton (Great Britain), M. G. N. Hine (Great Britain), L. van Hove (Belgium), K. Johnsen (Norway), M. Kaftanov (USSR), W. Klein (Holland), F. Krienen (Holland), Th. Kroeverath (German Federal Republic), C. Mallet (France), S. van der Meer (Holland), Mme. E. de Modzelewska-Bertrand (Switzerland), C. De Mol (Holland), J. Mussard (France), M. Pentz (Great Britain), G. Plass (German Federal Republic), P. Preiswerk (Switzerland), C. A. Ramm (Great Britain), C. Reinharz (Austria), F. de Rose (France), M. Salmeron (Brazil), A. Schoch (German Federal Republic), N. Spoonley (Great Britain), Miss E. W. D. Steel (Great Britain), R. Stierlin (Switzerland), W. Thirring (Austria), P. Tirion (Holland), Mme. S. Tixier (France), G. Vanderhaeghe (Belgium)

JOINT INSTITUTE FOR NUCLEAR RESEARCH

D. Danin (USSR), F. Florov (USSR), D. Granin (USSR), H. Keiser (German Democratic Republic), J. Kladnitzkaja (USSR), Korschig (Poland), M. Lebedenko (USSR), Muchin (USSR), Nguyen van Hieu (Vietnam), A. Nikitin (USSR), B. Pontecorvo (USSR), M. K. Scherbakova (USSR), L. Smirnova (USSR), T. Soprounoff (USSR), V. I. Veksler (USSR), F. Zakhartschenko (USSR)

BROOKHAVEN NATIONAL LABORATORY

Ch. Andersen, R. Philips, R. Rau, L. Salant

ACKNOWLEDGMENTS

INTERNATIONAL ATOMIC ENERGY AGENCY

P. Fent, V. S. Emelyanov, L. Lind

For comments on the manuscript I should like to thank:
G. Anders (Vienna), F. Bondy (Paris), M. Esslin (London), F. and L. Fischer (Vienna), U. Ibler (Bern), H. Kluter (Munich), W. Wollenberger (Zurich), and especially my wife.

INDEX

INDEX

About
the
Author

Robert Jungk, the eminent European journalist who has reported many of the important news stories of our time, was born in Berlin, Germany, in 1913 and acquired his Ph.D. in modern history at Zurich University. An American citizen since 1950, he lived for a time in Los Angeles but now makes his home in Vienna, Austria. He has been described by critics as one of the few writers who is trying successfully to bridge the gap between science and society, proof of which can be found in *The Big Machine* and in his previous best-selling books, *Tomorrow Is Already Here* and *Brighter Than a Thousand Suns,* which were published in more than a dozen countries. Dr. Jungk says: "My most important aim is to work toward the humanization of modern technology."